LIPPINCOTT

Phonics

Level B

**McGraw-Hill
School Division**

NEW YORK   FARMINGTON

Program Consultant

Mark E. Jewell, Ph.D.
Reading/Language Arts Coordinator
Highline Public Schools
Burien, Washington

Alphabet Font Used With Permission of Zaner-Bloser.

McGraw-Hill School Division
A Division of The McGraw·Hill Companies

McGraw-Hill School Division
1221 Avenue of the Americas
New York, New York 10020

Printed in the United States of America

ISBN 0-02-184469-0 / 1, L. B

1 2 3 4 5 6 7 8 9 POH 02 01 00 99 98 97

Contents

a_e

ate	hate	cane	mane	cape
made	same	came	game	name
take	bake	wake	pale	skate

a_e

Name _____

Color each picture whose name has the long **a** sound as in **cane**.

cane

 Helping at Home Your child is learning to recognize words with the letter pattern *a-consonant-e*.
Print *e* on a small card. Then write words such as: *can, at, mad, Sam, cap,* and *pal,* each on a different
card. Have your child put the cards together and read aloud: *cane, ate, made, same, cape,* and *pale*.

6   Introducing /ā/ a_e

Sam
Takes the Cape

by Tom Fen
pictures by Steve Haefele

"It is not a cap, but a mane gets flat under a cap," said Sam.

"The cape is fun. I will take the cape."

Helping at Home Your child has read this book in school. Read the book together at home. Then act out the parts of the clerk and the lion together.

8

2

"I want a cap," said Sam.
"I will go in."

Hats,
Caps, and
Capes

The man came back with a cape.
"Put it on," said the man. "It is not a cap, but it is black."

Sam put on the cape. It did not make his mane flat.

7

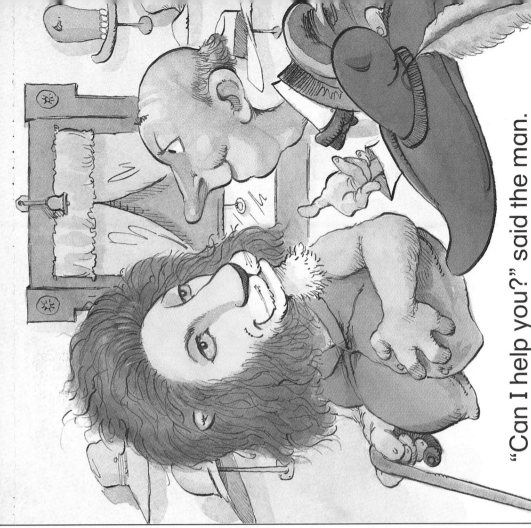

"Can I help you?" said the man.

"I want a black cap," Sam said.

"I have lots of hats and caps," said the man. He handed Sam a red hat.

"I do not want the cap," said Sam. "Take it back."

The man went to the rack in the back.

Sam put on the hat. "No, no," said Sam. "Take it back. I want a black cap."

"Do not get mad," said the man. "I will get a black cap."

4

The man went to the rack and got a black cap. Sam put it on.

Sam did not want the cap. It made his mane flat.

McGraw-Hill School Division

5

a_e

Circle the missing letters. Then write them. Read the word.

1.
ap
~~ape~~

c ape

2.
ape
ap

t ____

3.
an
ane

m ____

4.
ate
at

f ____

5.
ame
am

S ____

6.
an
ane

pl ____

Helping at Home To give your child practice with words that have the *a-consonant-e* structure, write silly sentences using as many such words as you can. Examples: *Jake gave the cake to a snake.* Have your child read and illustrate each sentence.

Name _____

Circle the word that names each picture.
Write the word.

| 1. | cake (circled) / cart | 2. | cape / hat | 3. | bell / tub |

c a k e

| 4. | sick / clock | 5. | skunk / drink | 6. | web / bubbles |

| 7. | fork / snake | 8. | lake / clown | 9. | town / draw |

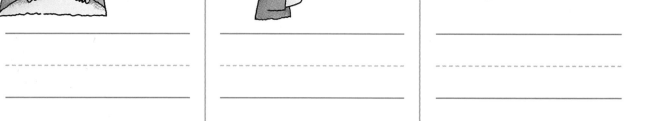

🏠 **Helping at Home** To help your child practice writing words, say the following: *cake, pink, sack, fawn, frown.* Ask your child to write a word that rhymes with each word you say. Possible responses: *take, lake; sink, rink; back, pack; dawn, lawn; down, crown.*

are

dare	hare	rare	bare	care
fare	mare	scare	flare	glare
Clare	blare	spare	stare	hardware

are

Write **are** under each picture whose name has the same ending sound as **hare**. Draw lines to match the letters.

hare

1.

_____

~~are~~

2.

_____

3.

_____

4.

_____

are

5.

_____

6.

_____

7.

_____

8.

_____

McGraw-Hill School Division

 Helping at Home Your child is learning to read and write words with the letters *are*. Write the following letters, each on a different card: *b, bl, c, d, f, fl, gl, h, r, sc, sp, st*. Have your child choose cards and use them to write words with *are*.

It is a hard trip, but Clare and her car get to the show.

Crowds stare. The car is a star!

CLARE and her CAR

by Sharon Gordon

illustrated by Barbara Friedman

Clare has a rare car. Crowds stare at her and her car.

Now Clare can go to the Rare Car Show. It is not far now!

Clare wants to go to the Rare Car Show. But, the rare car has mud on it!

How can Clare go now?

Clare cannot go. Her car is stuck. How can Clare get to the Rare Car Show now?

Clare must care for her rare car.
Clare gets a Car Care Kit. Clare
can rub the mud off.
Now Clare can go to the Rare
Car Show.

How can Clare go now? The rare
car has a flat. Clare sets up a flare
and gets the spare.

Clare wants to go to the Rare
Car Show. But, the rare car has
mud on it!

How can Clare go now?

Clare cannot go. Her car is stuck.
How can Clare get to the Rare Car
Show now?

Clare must care for her rare car.
Clare gets a Car Care Kit. Clare
can rub the mud off.
Now Clare can go to the Rare
Car Show.

How can Clare go now? The rare
car has a flat. Clare sets up a flare
and gets the spare.

Name_____

are

Color the pictures whose names have the same ending sound as **scare**. Write **are**.

scare

1.	2.	3.	4.
are			

5.	6.	7.	8.

 Helping at Home Make an *are* "hopscotch" game on a small sheet of paper. Write a word with *are* in each square. Examples: *hare, rare, dare, care, fare, spare, bare, scare, glare.* Have your child say each word as he or she throws a marker and jumps from square to square.

Circle the missing letters. Then write them.
Read the word.

1.

(ane)

ake

m _ane_

2.

ate

are

b _____

3.

ll

lp

hi_____

4.

ape

are

c _____

5.

cr

br

_____own

6.

ck

nk

sku_____

McGraw-Hill School Division

e
ee

he	be	me	we
see	bee	tree	keep
deep	sleep	seed	feed
need	meet	feet	street
feel	green	week	needs

e
ee

Name_____

Color each picture whose name has the long **e** sound as in **me** and **bee**.

me

bee

Helping at Home Write the following words with long *e* on index cards: *bee, tree, seed, feed, feet, meet, keep, jeep, he, we, green, teen.* Mix the cards and place them face down, in rows. Take turns picking up two cards and reading the words. Ask your child to say "beep beep!" if the words rhyme.

22   Introducing /ē/ *e, ee*

e ee	

Me and **bee** have the long **e** sound.
Read the word. Circle the picture that the
word names.

Name_____

me    bee

1. he	 
2. eel	  
3. we	  
4. green	  

 Helping at Home Write the following long e words for your child to practice reading: *we, he, be, deep, seen, keep, secret* and *me*. Have your child choose a couple of the words to illustrate and then label the drawings with the words.

e
ee

Circle the word that names each picture.

1.

(feed)　　barn

2.

he　　　me

3.

bell　　　bee

4.

peel　　　pal

5.

heel　　　he

6.

tree　　　ten

7.

weed　　　we

8.

paw　　　peek

9.

seed　　　be

Helping at Home To help your child recognize words with the long *e* sound of *e* and *ee*, write the following word endings on pieces of paper: *e, ee, eed, eet, eep, een, eel.* Together write words that can be made with these endings.

The SEED

by
Louisa Ernesto
illustrated by
David Scott Meier

Keep the seeds all winter.
In summer, plant the seeds.
The little seeds will go
up and up . . . .
up to ten feet.
Can it be?
I was a little seed.

 Helping at Home Your child has read this book in
school. Have him or her read it aloud to you. Then discuss
what a seed needs to grow into a plant.

8

See me?
I am a little seed.
I need to be in the garden.
Plant me deep. Plant me deep.

McGraw-Hill School Division

For weeks and weeks I go up, up,
and up to ten feet.
Do you see me?
Now I have lots of seeds.
You can pick up the seeds.

Now you cannot see me.
I start to go up.
And I start to go deep, deep, deep down.

Pull the weeds.
I need to feel the sun.
Tall weeds keep the sun off me.
Get rid of all the weeds.

I feel the sun.
It warms me, and I pop up.
I have a green stem.
Can you see it?

4

McGraw-Hill School Division

Now help me.
Water me.
Water me well.

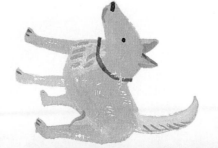

5

ee

Name the first picture in each row.
Circle the pictures whose names have
the same long **e** sound. Write **ee**.

 Helping at Home Go for a walk and play the game "I See" with your child. Look for objects whose names have the *ee* sound, and finish the sentence *I see a _____.* For example: *I see a bee.* *I see a wheel.*

Practicing /ē/ *ee*   29

e
ee

Choose the word that completes
the sentence. Write the word.

| He | sees | We | green | feet |

1.
Wade _____s̶e̶e̶s̶_____ a big hat.

2.
The hat is _____ .

3.
_____ wants to keep it.

4.
_____ do not want to get the hat.

5.
Wade gets socks for his _____ .

Helping at Home Help your child practice listening for the sound of long *e*. Say sentences
containing long *e* words, such as: *Even zebras keep secrets.* Have him or her clap each time he or
she hears the sound of long *e*.

Name_____

Circle the word that names each picture.
Write the word.

1. feed
     glare

f e e d

2. hare
     farm

3. table
     cane

4. ate
     hat

5. gate
     seeds

6. mare
     far

7. tree
     bee

8. beep
     street

9. me
     rare

 Helping at Home Write these words on index cards: *kitten, mask, bark, luck, wink, drink, made, mane, cape, hare, Clare, Mark, he, be, me, see, keep, feed.* Help your child use the words to dictate a story to you. He or she might tell about a pet store, for example.

Fill in the circle in front of the missing letters.
Then write them. Read the word.

1. ○ are
● ee

_____
gr__ee__n

2. ○ e
○ ee

_____
m_____

3. ○ ake
○ are

_____
h_____

4. ○ ate
○ are

_____
sk_____

5. ○ le
○ ee

_____
f_____t

6. ○ ane
○ ape

_____
c_____

 Helping at Home Your child has been learning to read words with *a-consonant-e*, *are*, *e*, and *ee*. Ask your child to imagine a hare with green feet. Encourage your child to use as many words with *a-consonant-e*, *are*, *e*, and *ee* as possible in describing it.

ea

eat	seat	meat	beat	heat
treat	read	leap	mean	bean
tea	sea	seal	meal	leaf
dream	east	feast	least	repeat

Name _____

ea

Write **ea**. Color each picture whose name has the long **e** sound as in **seal**.

seal

- - - - - e a -

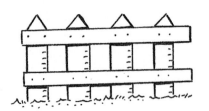

McGraw-Hill School Division

 Helping at Home Help your child practice reading words with *ea* as in *seal*. Write these words on slips of paper: *east, sea, seat, feast, dream, treat, heat,* and *eat*. Take turns choosing a slip of paper, reading the word, and making up a silly sentence.

Dinner in the Garden

by Anne W. Phillips

illustrated by Susan Swan

"Have a leaf," said the little bug
to his mom. "A leaf is a neat treat!
I will eat and eat and eat."

Helping at Home Your child has read this book in
school. Help him or her to read it to you. Then have your
child name vegetables that he or she likes.

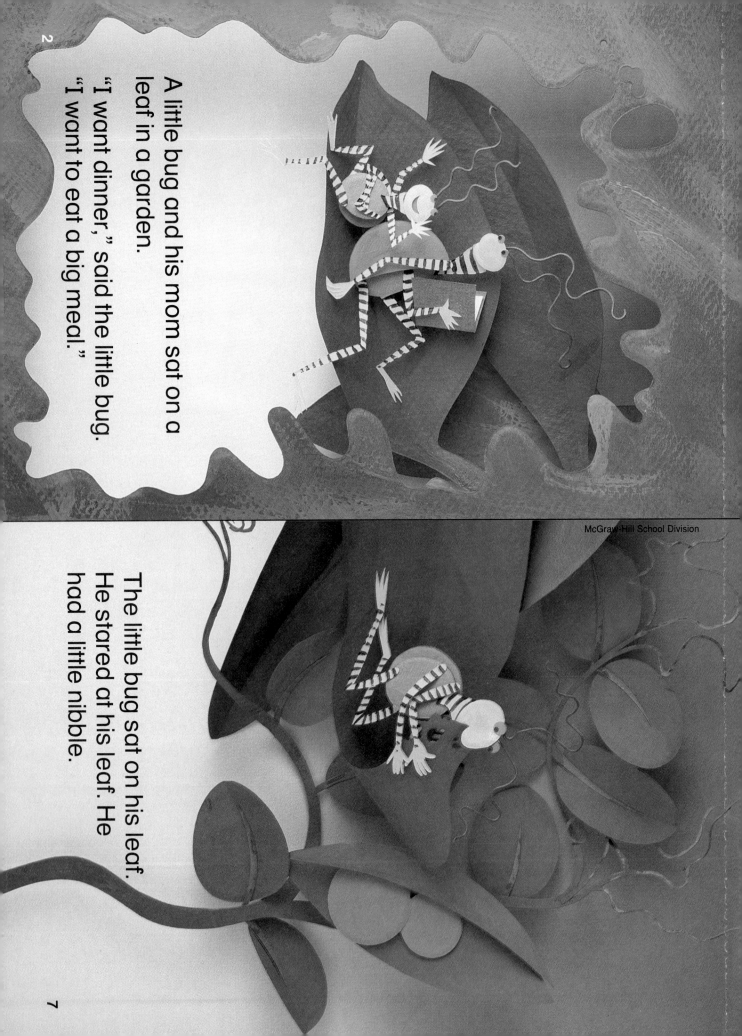

A little bug and his mom sat on a leaf in a garden.

"I want dinner," said the little bug.

"I want to eat a big meal."

The little bug sat on his leaf. He stared at his leaf. He had a little nibble.

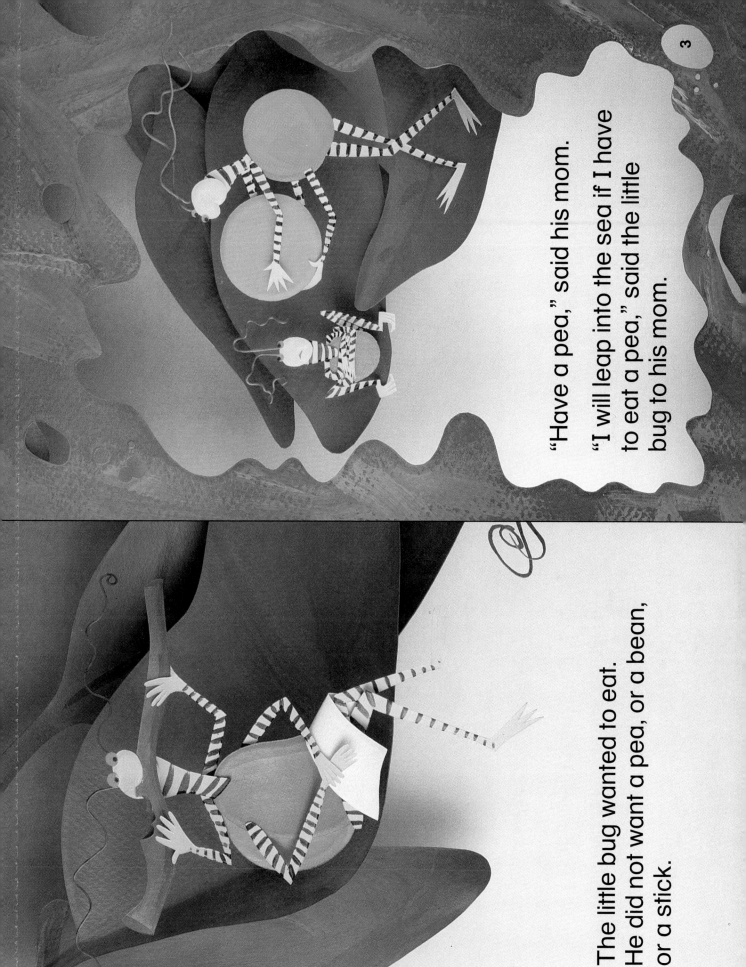

"Have a pea," said his mom.

"I will leap into the sea if I have to eat a pea," said the little bug to his mom.

The little bug wanted to eat.
He did not want a pea, or a bean, or a stick.

4

"Have a bean," said his mom.
"I will act mean if I have
to eat a bean," said the little
bug to his mom.

McGraw-Hill School Division

"Have a stick," said his mom.
"I will scream ICK ICK if I have
to eat a stick," said the little bug
to his mom.
"Fuss, fuss, fuss," said his mom.

5

ea

Name_____

Color the pictures whose names have the long **e** sound as in **meat**. Write **ea**.

meat

1.	2.	3.	4.
e a			

5.	6.	7.	8.

 Helping at Home To help your child practice reading and writing words with *ea*, play "Change-a-Word." Have your child write one of these words: *beat, mean, heat, bean, seat, seal, meat*. Tell him or her to change one letter—either the first or the last—to make a new word.

Name_____

Circle the missing letters. Then write them.
Read the word.

1.
i
(ee)

b  t

2.
ea
a

l_____ f

3.
ane
are

c_____

4.
ake
are

m_____

5.
e
ee

b_____

6.
e
ea

r_____ d

 Helping at Home Help your child search for words in books, magazines, and newspapers that have the long *e* sound made with *e, ee,* and *ea.* He or she may want to make a long *e* tree. On a leaf, write each long *e* word your child recognizes, then hang the leaf on a branch marked *e, ea,* or *ee.*

McGraw-Hill School Division

ai

aim	mail	tail	fail	pail
sail	nail	hail	snail	trail
rain	pain	brain	train	plain
drain	paint	paid	wait	waist

ai

Name _____

Write **ai**. Color each picture whose name has the long **a** sound as in **train**.

train

ai

Helping at Home To help your child practice recognizing words with the *ai* sound as in *train*, try making up zany weather reports together. You might use these words in your report: *rain, hail, drain, waist, pail, wait, sail.*

The Painter

by Leya Roberts
illustrated by Bernard Adnet

"The train, the snail, and the sail are *not* plain now!" said Frog with a grin.

"And *I* am not plain! Wow!"

 Helping at Home Your child has read this book in school. Read it together at home. Then you might enjoy painting a picture together.

8

Frog had pails of paint—
a pail of black paint,
a pail of brown paint,
a pail of red paint,
a pail of green paint,
and a pail of pink paint.
"I will paint," said Frog.

McGraw-Hill School Division

It started to rain. Trails of paint ran
down the paper.

Drip, drip, drip.

"I can paint a snail," said Frog.
So she painted a black snail.
"I can paint a train," she said.
She painted a brown train.

Frog added red paint to the train.
She added green paint to the
snail. And she added pink paint
to the sail.
"It is better now," said Frog.
"But it is still plain."

"I can paint a sail," said Frog.
She painted a red sail.

Frog stopped. "The train, the snail
and the sail are plain!" she said.

"But wait," she said, "I can make
them better."

ai

Choose the word that completes the sentence. Write the word.

| trail | drain | aim | mail | snail |

1. Water went down the _drain_ .

2. I can _____ the letter.

3. The _____ is small.

4. Keep on the _____ .

5. You can _____ for the spot.

Helping at Home Your child has been learning to read and write words with the *ai* sound. Have your child write these words: *pail, braid, drain, sail, train,* and *paid.* Then have him or her say the pairs of rhyming words.

Name_____

Fill in the circle in front of the word that
names each picture. Write the word.

I. 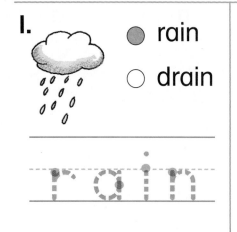 ● rain
○ drain

rain

2.  ○ tail
○ pail

3.  ○ feast
○ least

4.  ○ care
○ hare

5. ○ sleep
○ seal

6.  ○ fade
○ feed

7.  ○ wait
○ waist

8.  ○ scar
○ scare

9. ○ plane
○ pleat

 Helping at Home You might want to help your child make a word journal. This can be a
place to record words that he or she knows how to write, words that might be confusing *(meat, meet),*
or words that your child simply enjoys.

McGraw-Hill School Division

i i_e
ie

find	kind	mind	grind	blind
line	nine	pine	fine	ride
side	hide	fire	tire	pile
smile	bite	kite	like	time
pie	tie	tied	tried	cried

i

Name_____

Write **i** under each picture whose name has the long **i** sound as in **find**.
Draw lines to match the letters.

find

1.

2.

3.

4.

i

5.

6.

7.

8.

McGraw-Hill School Division

 Helping at Home Your child has begun to learn the long *i* sound as in *kind*. Write the following long *i* words on a card: *find, kind, wind, mind*. Encourage your child to use the words in a finger puppet show.

Introducing / ī / i

ie

Pie has the long **i** sound.
Read each word. Circle the picture that the word names.

pie

1. lie	
2. tie	
3. tied	
4. cried	

 Helping at Home In addition to learning about *ie* as an ending sound, your child is learning about the sound *ie* makes in words such as *tied, tried, fries, fried,* and *cried.* See if he or she can make up one or two sentences using these words.

Name_____

i_e

Circle the pictures whose names have the same long **i** sound as in **nine**. Write **i** and **e**.

nine **9**

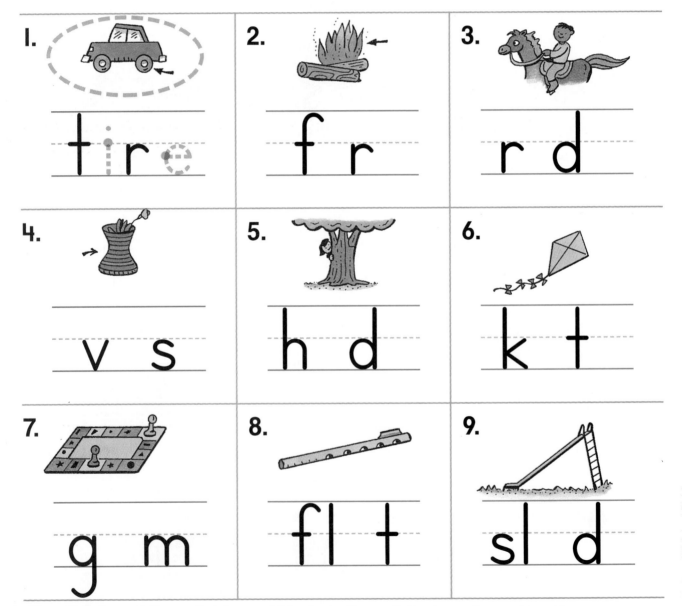

1.	2.	3.
t i r e	f _ r	r _ d
4.	**5.**	**6.**
v _ s	h _ d	k _ t
7.	**8.**	**9.**
g _ m	f l _ t	s l _ d

McGraw-Hill School Division

 Helping at Home To help your child understand how a silent *e* changes the vowel sound in a word, write these words on paper: *fin, hid, kit, dim, pin, rid,* and *bit.* Now have your child add an *e* to each word and read the new word.

The Summer Fran Tried CAMP

by Robin Bloksberg
illustrated by Lisa Blackshear

At the end of the summer, Fran hugged all the kids. She cried a little.

Fran had such a fine time at camp. She didn't want to go!

 Helping at Home Your child has read this book in school. Take turns reading it aloud. Have your child tell how Fran felt about camp at the beginning and at the end of the story.

8

The summer Fran was nine, she went to camp.

Mom and Dad smiled and hugged her. Fran tried to smile, too. But she cried, a little.

McGraw-Hill School Division

The campers went for a ride in a wagon.

Fran sat at the campfire. She was tired but she had a smile on her face.

Fran tried not to be sad.
She went to find her tent. It had
bunk beds!

Fran liked her bed. It was fun
to lie in!

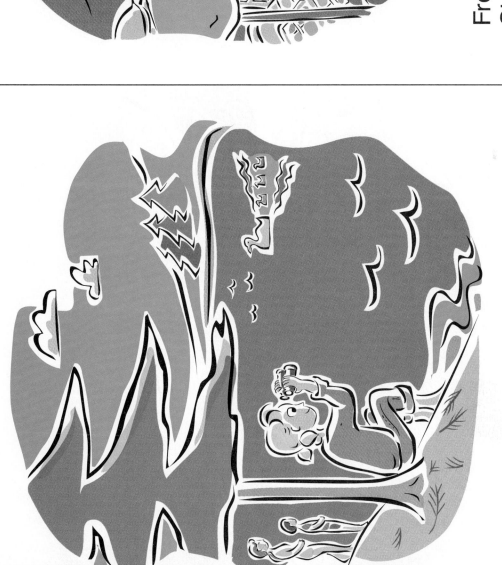

Fran sat under a pine tree. She
tried to find a duck. Camp
was fine.

Fran lined up for dinner and ate
and ate.
"Pile on the pie!" Fran said.

4

At camp, Fran ran for miles and
miles. She got a kite. She had fun.

5

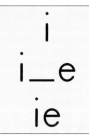

i
i_e
ie

Name_____

Circle the word that names each picture.

1. mind   (find)

2. pie   pine

3. rid   ride

4. tried   tie

5. line   lied

6. kind   wind

7. tire   mind

8. lie   tied

9. slide   kite

Helping at Home Have your child draw an imaginary creature. Have him or her tell things the creature might do, using as many long *i* words as possible. Examples: *bite some fruit, find a dime.* Then have your child say some of the long *i* words he or she used.

i
i__e
ie

Name _____

Choose the word that completes the sentence. Write the word.

| pie | dried | kite | find | hide |

1.

Todd draws a ___kite___ .

2.

Ann likes to _____ .

3.

We eat _____ .

4.

Can you _____ Ann?

5.

Hands are _____ .

McGraw-Hill School Division

 Helping at Home To help your child practice words with long *i*, have a tie-decorating contest! Draw large neckties. Then challenge your child to decorate the tie with pictures whose names have the long *i* sound.

Name_____

Circle the word that names each picture.
Write the word.

1. 10¢ dare (dime) _dime_	**2.** pail peel	**3.** find wind
4. meat mail	**5.** kind hike	**6.** pie lie
7. beets beans	**8.** fail feet	**9.** pin pine

 Helping at Home Help your child cut out a kite from construction or wrapping paper to hang on the wall. Now have your child write, on strips of paper, all of the long *i* words he or she can think of. Attach these strips to the kite to make a tail.

Name_____

Circle the missing letters. Then write them.
Read the word.

I.

ie

ame

t i e

2.

ai

ee

sl____p

3.

ie

ea

____gle

4.

ai

ee

n____l

5.

ine

ail

n____

6.

ai

ea

tr____n

 Helping at Home Have your child draw his or her own pretend amusement park. Suggest that your child post signs on the rides. When he or she is finished, talk about the words and the vowel sounds they make.

McGraw-Hill School Division

ir

sir	stir	bird	girl	dirt
Kirk	skirt	first	twirl	swirl

ir	Name _____
	Circle the pictures whose names have the sound of **ir** as in **girl**. Write **ir**.

girl

1. _____ _____	2. _____ _____	3. _____ _____
4. _____ _____	5. _____ _____	6. _____ _____
7. _____ _____	8. _____ _____	9. _____ _____

McGraw-Hill School Division

 Helping at Home To help your child to become familiar with the *ir* sound, write the following words: *sir, stir, girl, dirt, first, twirl.* Then together, build a story that uses these words.

Madam Pig and Sir Kirk

by Leya Roberts

illustrated by Pat Hoggan

Madam Pig met Sir Kirk.

"You dressed up," Sir Kirk said.

"I did," said Madam Pig. "And you did, too!"

"Mmm!" said Madam Pig and Sir Kirk.

 Helping at Home Your child has read this funny story in school. Have him or her read it aloud. Then ask your child to tell why Madam Pig got dirt all over herself.

8

"Sir Kirk will be here. I must get dressed," said Madam Pig.
"First I need a skirt."

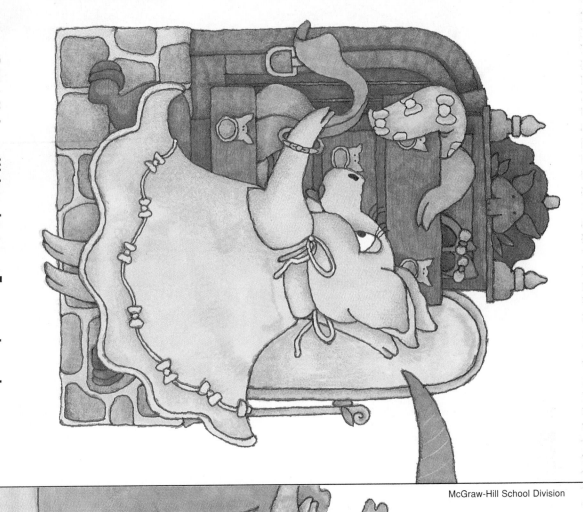

"I need dirt!" cried Madam Pig.
She ran and plopped in the dirt.
"A pig needs dirt! Now I am all set!" said Madam Pig.

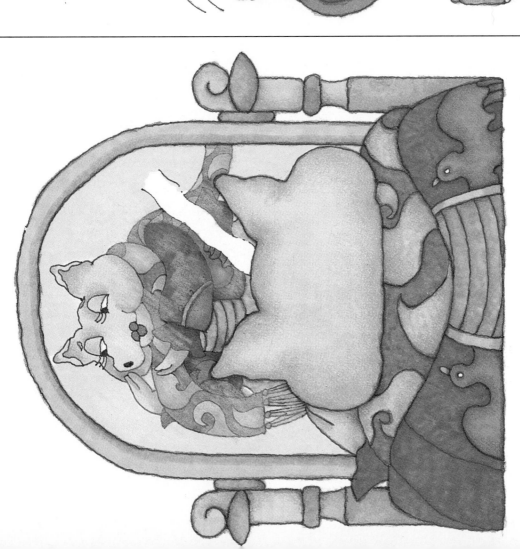

Madam Pig put on her skirt. She spun and twirled. "I like the skirt," she said. "But I need a nice top, too."

Madam Pig stopped and frowned. "Hmm, a skirt, a top with birds, a scarf with swirls. I need . . ." Madam Pig started.

4

Madam Pig put on a top with red birds on it. She spun and twirled. "I like this top," she said. "But I need a scarf, too."

Madam Pig put on a scarf with pink swirls. She spun and twirled. "I like this scarf with the pink swirls," she said.

5

ir

Name _____

Color the pictures whose names have the sound of **ir** as in **dirt**. Write **ir**.

dirt

1.

_____
ir

2.

_____

3.

_____

4.

_____

5.

_____

6.

_____

7.

_____

8.

_____

 Helping at Home Encourage your child to make up a new dance step. Have him or her name the dance step using one or more words that have the same *ir* sound as in *bird*. Examples: *twirl, swirl, whirl, first, squirrel*.

Name_____

Circle the word that names each picture.
Write the word.

1. 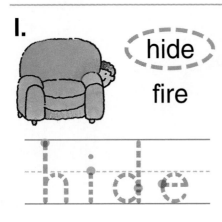 (hide) fire

hide

2.  bee mane

_____

3.  late leaf

_____

4.  seem skirt

_____

5.  lie we

_____

6.  bait bird

_____

7.  girl grain

_____

8.  bell mail

_____

9.  rain first

_____

Helping at Home Help your child practice reading and writing words by writing a short note or letter to a friend or family member. Have your child read the completed letter aloud to you before sending it.

McGraw-Hill School Division

ir

Color the pictures whose names have the sound of **ir** as in **dirt**. Write **ir**.

dirt

1.	2.	3.	4.
_ir_			

5.	6.	7.	8.

 Helping at Home Encourage your child to make up a new dance step. Have him or her name the dance step using one or more words that have the same *ir* sound as in *bird*. Examples: *twirl, swirl, whirl, first, squirrel.*

Name_____

Circle the word that names each picture.
Write the word.

I. 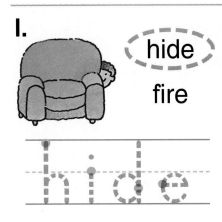 (hide) fire	**2.**  bee mane	**3.**  late leaf
h i d e		
4.  seem skirt	**5.**  lie we	**6.**  bait bird
7. girl grain	**8.** bell mail	**9.** rain first

Helping at Home Help your child practice reading and writing words by writing a short note or letter to a friend or family member. Have your child read the completed letter aloud to you before sending it.

McGraw-Hill School Division

o
o_e

go	no	so	old	fold
gold	told	cold	hold	bold
note	hole	pole	rode	rose
nose	hose	home	poke	smoke
rope	cone	stone	alone	open

O

Write **o**. Color each picture whose name has the long **o** sound as in **hold**.

hold

O

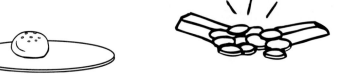

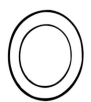

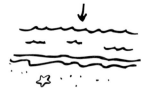

 Helping at Home Your child has been introduced to words with the long *o* sound. Help your child to remember this sound by encouraging him or her to write a poem using these words: *go, no, so, old, gold, told, cold, hold.*

o_e

Circle the pictures whose names have the long **o** sound as in **rope**. Write **o** and **e**.

rope

1. h o l e

2. c _ n

3. g _ m

4. l _ m

5. p l _

6. n _ s

7. h _ s

8. n _ n

9. b _ n

 Helping at Home Write these letters at the top of a sheet of paper: *b, r, n, m, l, h, p, s, o*, and *e*. Help your child write words that have the long *o* sound, using those letters. Examples: *robe, bone, home, nose, rose*.

Name _____

Name the first picture in each row. Circle the pictures whose names have the same long **o** sound.

1.

2.

3.

4.

5.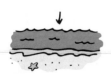

Helping at Home Say a long *o* word, such as *go* or *stone*. Have your child name a rhyming word. Then have him or her think of another long *o* word for you to rhyme. Examples: *gold, old, told, bold; zero, hero; go, no, piano.*

McGraw-Hill School Division

THE HUNT FOR A COLD NOSE

by Susan McCloskey

illustrated by Marie-Louise Gay

Go to the stone frog

Peg let Ned hold the pup.

"I get it," said Peg. "The pup has a cold nose!"

Helping at Home Your child has read this book. Have him or her read it aloud. Then, together, you might want to write simple directions for a "fun" hunt in your own house.

Mom handed Peg a note. The note said, **Go to the stone frog.**

"A hunt!" said Ned. "It will be fun!"

Go to the stone frog.

Peg hunted inside. She came back out. She was not alone!

"A pup!" she cried. "Ned! We got a pup!"

"The stone frog is in the garden," said Peg. "It is near the hose."

Ned and Peg ran to the frog. Under it, they saw a note. The note said, **Now hunt for a gold rose.**

3

Ned felt his nose.
"It isn't cold," he said. "A cold nose will be hard to find!"

"We can do it," Peg told him.

6

Ned and Peg hunted for the gold rose. Peg hunted under the old elm tree. Ned hunted near the flag pole.

"I see the note," said Ned. "It is in the hole Dad dug for the roses."

4

Ned got the note. The note said,
You got the notes at the stone frog and the gold rose. Now find a cold nose.

"A cold nose?" asked Ned.

You got the notes at the stone frog and the gold rose. Now find a cold nose.

5

Name_____

O

Color the pictures whose names have the long **o** sound as in **fold**. Write **o**.

fold

1.	2.	3.	4.
			14 K

5.	6.	7.	8.

 Helping at Home Have your child look for long *o* words the next time you're taking a walk or driving in the car. Some of the words he or she might spot are: *go, sold, old,* and *toll*.

o_e

Name_____

Choose the word that completes the sentence. Write the word.

pole	rose	stone	mole	rope

1.

I can tie the  _____ .

2.

The _____ likes to dig.

3.

I can smell the _____ .

4.

The flag is on the _____ .

5.

The girl has a _____ .

 Helping at Home To provide practice with long *o* words, together think up silly phrases or sentences with the long *o* sound, such as: *Mole rode home. Go, gold nose.*

McGraw-Hill School Division

Name_____

Fill in the circle in front of the missing letters.
Then write them. Read the word.

I.

● o
○ i

g___ld

2.

○ ie
○ ir

b_____d

3.

○ ine
○ ole

n_____

4.

○ ai
○ o

t___l

5.

○ ise
○ ose

r_____

6.

○ ee
○ ai

tr_____

 Helping at Home Help your child search through old magazines to find words with long *a* (*game, pail*), long *e* (*seat, tree*), long *i* (*bike*), or long *o* (*rope*) sounds. Have him or her glue the words to paper and draw pictures to go with each one.

Circle the word that names each picture.
Write the word.

1.    cane

(cone)

c o n e

2.   smoke

stone

3.    sand

seal

4.   ride

rose

5.   cried

pie

6.   paint

train

7.   snake

fake

8.   open

rope

9.   girl

twirl

Helping at Home Draw a triple-scoop ice-cream cone. Help your child think of words with long *a, e, i,* and *o*. In the first scoop, write long *a* words. In the second scoop, write long *e* words. In the third scoop, write long *i* words. In the cone, write long *o* words. Add more words over time.

or
ore

or	for	fork	cork
horn	born	corn	acorn
cord	storm	afford	forget

more	sore	tore	bore
core	wore	score	before

or

Name _____

Write **or**. Color each picture whose name has the sound of **or** as in **fork**.

fork

o r

McGraw-Hill School Division

Helping at Home Give your child practice with *or* by helping her or him write words containing *or* on a sheet of paper. Then encourage your child to say some of the words in sentences. Possible words: *popcorn, born, torn, worn, snort, sport, short, cord,* and *porch*.

ore

Name _____

Write **ore** under each picture whose name has the same ending sound as **tore**.
Draw lines to match the letters.

tore

1.

_____
o r e

2.

_____

_____

3.

_____

_____

4.

_____

ore

5.

_____

6.

_____

_____

7.

_____

_____

8.

_____

_____

 Helping at Home Print *ore* on a small card. Then write the following letters, each on a different card: *c, t, w, s, m.* Help your child combine the cards to form such words as *core, tore, wore, sore, more, score, store.*

or ore

Name _____

Circle the word that names each picture.

1.
(fork)   fine

2.
ham   horn

3.
core   camp

4.
corn   cork

5.
stork   stone

6.
tore   wore

7.
stork   store

8.
score   sore

9.
snore   more

Helping at Home Write silly sentences using as many *or* and *ore* words as you can. Examples: *My feet were sore even before I wore the new shoes from the store. Or, Norm eats popcorn with a fork.* Have your child read and illustrate each sentence.

ore

Name _____

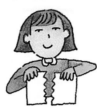

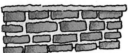

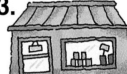

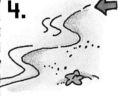

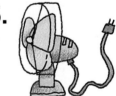

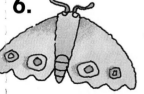

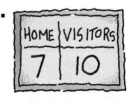

McGraw-Hill School Division

Score More

by
Johanna Richard

photos by
Amy and Richard
Hutchings

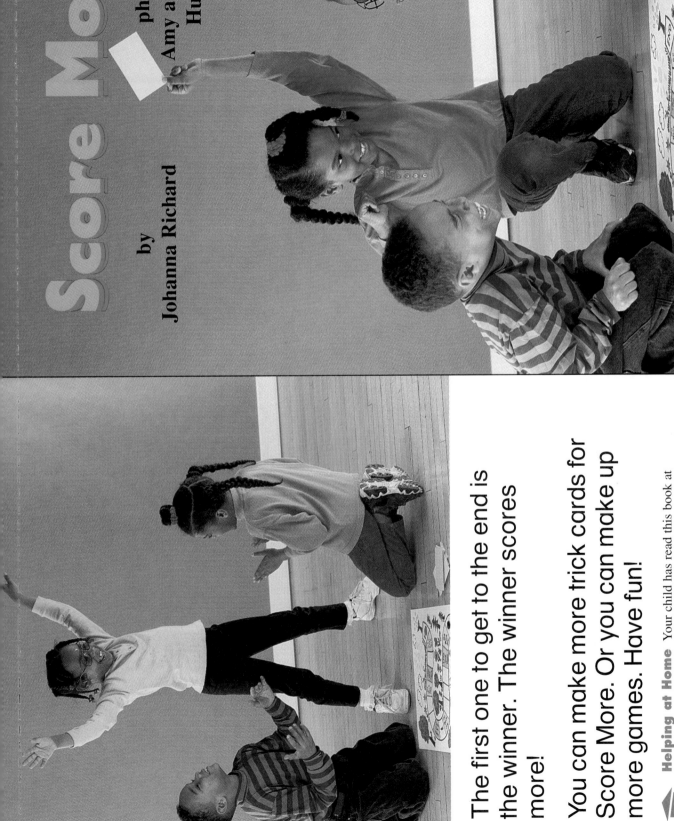

The first one to get to the end is the winner. The winner scores more!

You can make more trick cards for Score More. Or you can make up more games. Have fun!

Score More is a fun game. It is a game you can afford. But you will not find Score More in a store. You can make Score More!

McGraw-Hill School Division

Now you can start!

1. Get two or more pals.
2. Pick a card. Do the trick.
3. If a pal can name the trick, go two blocks. If no one can name the trick, go back one block.
4. Pass the cards to the pal on your left.

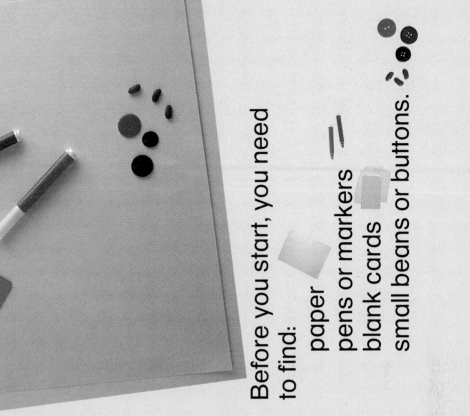

Before you start, you need to find:

paper
pens or markers
blank cards
small beans or buttons.

Hold a fork.

Be popcorn! Pop! Pop! Pop!

Go to sleep.

Eat an apple.

Now make cards. Think of tricks for you and your pals to do. Print the tricks on the cards. Put the cards in a pile.

4

Score More has a trail. How do you want to draw your trail? You can draw two lines that twist and twirl. You pick! Score More is your game.

Draw blocks inside the lines. Mark Leap Two More on five blocks. Mark Go Back One on five or more blocks. Do not forget to mark End on the last block.

You can draw on your game if you want. Make a garden or a park.

5

or

Name_____

Color the pictures whose names have the sound of **or** as in **fork**. Write **or**.

fork

1.

2.

3.

4.

or

5.

6.

7.

8.

 Helping at Home Your child is learning words with *or*. Help him or her find items around the home whose names contain this letter combination. If possible, help your child label the items. Possible items: *corn, fork, popcorn, cork, porch, sports equipment, pitchfork,* and *cord*.

ore

Name _____

Circle the word that names each picture.

1.

(store) wore

2.

scare score

3.

cone core

4.

tire tore

5.

snore sore

6.

more corn

7.

sore same

8.

wore wire

9.

bore before

 Helping at Home Write words with *ore*, each on a separate card. Examples: *more, store, core, score, tore, sore, before, snore, wore.* Turn the cards face down. Help your child to choose a card, read the word, and use it in a sentence.

Name_____

Circle the missing letters. Then write them. Read the word.

1. ore air

st _ore_

2. ea ir

sk___t

3. or ai

dr___n

4. ee ai

sl___p

5. or ee

str___t

6. ea or

st___m

 Helping at Home Your child is learning to read and write words with *or* and *ore*. As you and your child read together at home, encourage her or him to point out words that contain these letter combinations as well as any words your child can read alone.

Name_____

Circle the word that names each picture.
Write the word.

1. 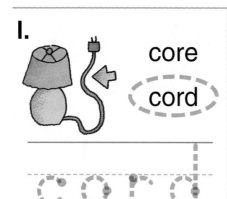 core

(cord)

cord

2.  seed

sled

3.  wore

score

4.  hard

heat

5. find

fire

6. stone

store

7.  twirl

twist

8. pie

pot

9. popcorn

acorn

McGraw-Hill School Division

oa
oe

oats	oak	boat	coat
loaf	soap	goat	toad
road	soak	float	boast
hoe	toe	toes	goes

oa
oe

Name _____

Color each picture whose name has the
long **o** sound as in **toad** and **goes**.

toad  goes

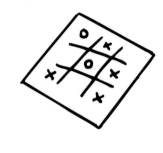

McGraw-Hill School Division

 Helping at Home Write words with *oa* and *oe*, such as *goal, toad, float, oak, hoe, toe,* and *goes*
on cards. Say a short sentence with one of the words, leaving out the *oa* or *oe* word. Ask your child to
hold up the card with the word that best completes the sentence.

94 Introducing /ō/ oa, oe

oa
oe

Name_____

Doe and **float** have the long **o** sound. Read each word. Circle the picture that the word names.

doe  float

1. toe			
2. boat			
3. hoe			
4. soap			

 Helping at Home To give your child practice reading words with *oe* and *oa*, stop at random words as you read a story together. Ask your child to give "thumbs up" if the words contain *oe* or *oa* with the long *o* sound and "thumbs down" if they do not.

Name _____

Circle the word that names each picture.

1.

(soap)   same

2.

he   hoe

3.

coat   float

4.

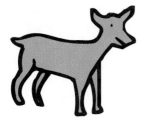

dime   doe

5.

game   goat

6.

toe   store

7.

oak   oats

8.

loan   loaf

9.

bone   boat

Helping at Home To help your child listen for the sound of long *o*, play "I Am Thinking of A Word." Say riddles, such as: *I am thinking of a word that rhymes with* goat. *It sails across the sea.* (*A boat*) Examples of words for riddles: *doe, soap, toe, loaf, hoe, toad.*

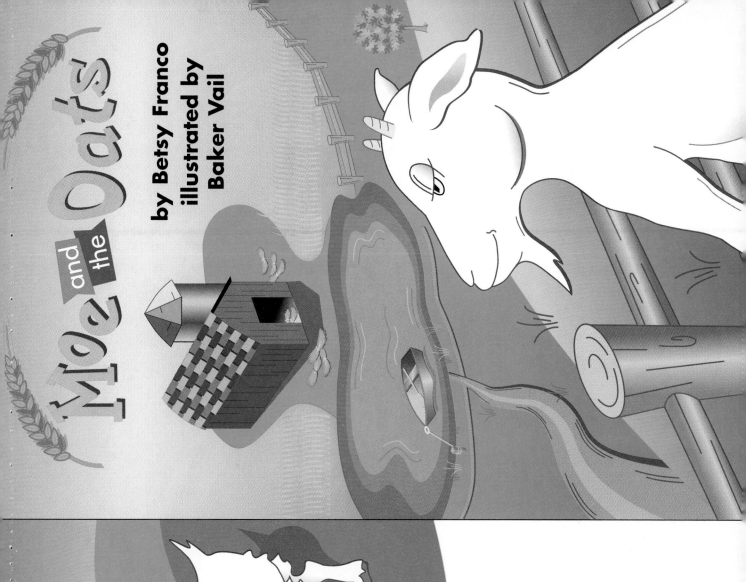

Moe and the Oats

by Betsy Franco
illustrated by Baker Vail

"No oats," Moe told his goat pals.
"But grass, pals, and a fine home
are better."

Moe the goat ate a big bite of
grass and smiled.

Helping at Home Your child has read this book in school. Have him or her read it aloud to you. Then discuss all the things Moe did to try to get some oats.

Moe the goat had a fine home.
He had goat pals. He had grass
to eat.

But Moe wanted more.
He wanted oats.

"Mmmm. Oats," he said.
"I like grass, but oats are better."

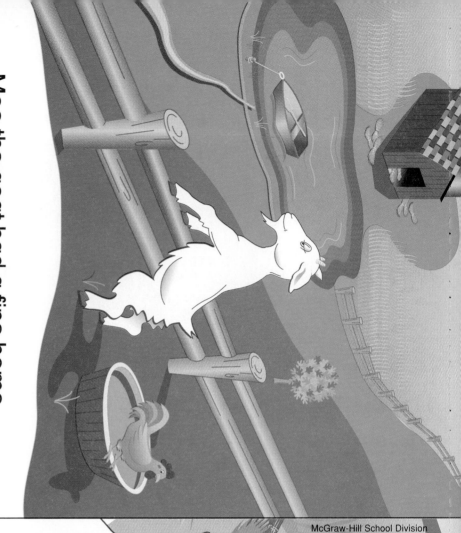

McGraw-Hill School Division

At last Moe came to the oats.
He saw people! The people had
hoes. A farmer loaded the oats
on a wagon.

No oats left for a goat! No oats
at all!

So Moe went home.

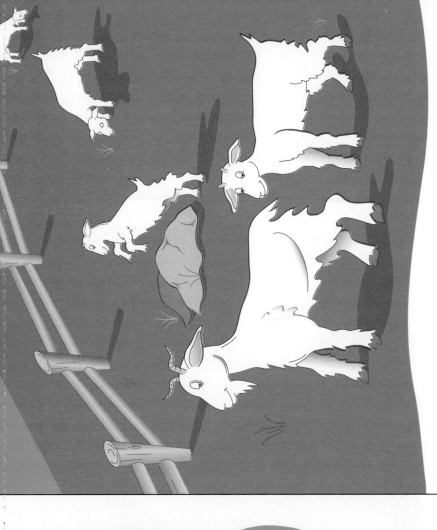

"I will cross the pond and get oats," Moe boasted. "We will have a big feast."

"Go, Moe, go!" said all of his goat pals.

"I will take the road," Moe said. "I want oats!"

"Go, Moe, go!" said his pals.

Moe the goat went down the road. The sun was hot. He felt roasted, but he went on.

Moe went to the pond.

"I will swim to the oats," he said.
"I don't care if I get soaked."

"Go, Moe, go!" said his pals.

Moe put his toes in the water.
But the pond was deep and cold.
It was too cold for a goat.

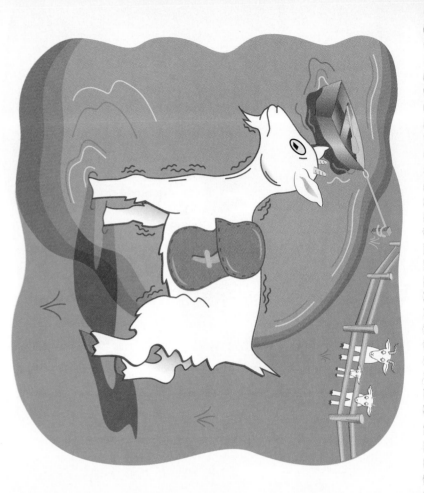

Moe saw a boat on the water.

"I will float in a boat to the oats,"
said Moe.

"Go, Moe, go!" said his pals.

Moe sat in the boat. But a goat like
Moe cannot make a boat go.

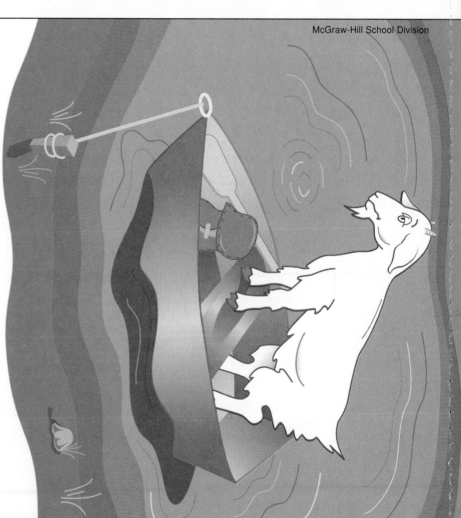

oa
oe

Name _____

Color the pictures whose names have the long **o** sound as in **toad** or **goes**.

1.	2.	3.	4.

5.	6.	7.	8.

9.	10.	11.	12.

 Helping at Home Give your child practice with long *o* by helping him or her write words containing *oa* and *oe* on a sheet of paper. Then encourage your child to say sentences using some of these words. Possible words to use: *toad, doe, goal, goat, soak, moan, hoe, oats, roast, toe, boast,* and *groan.*

oa
oe

Name _____

Choose the word that completes the sentence. Write the word.

| doe | float | goes | coat | goat |

1.  Ted puts on his  _____ .

2. A girl deer is a _____ .

3.  The _____ ate all the grass.

4.  See how the car _____ .

5.  I eat a cream soda _____ .

 Helping at Home To help your child practice recognizing words with the long *o* sound, take turns completing sentences with words containing the letter combinations *oa* and *oe*. Example: "The farmer weeded the field with a _____." (hoe) Possible words: *toe, toes, doe, floe, oboe, float, groan,* and *roast.*

McGraw-Hill School Division

Name_____

Circle the missing letters. Then write them. Read the word.

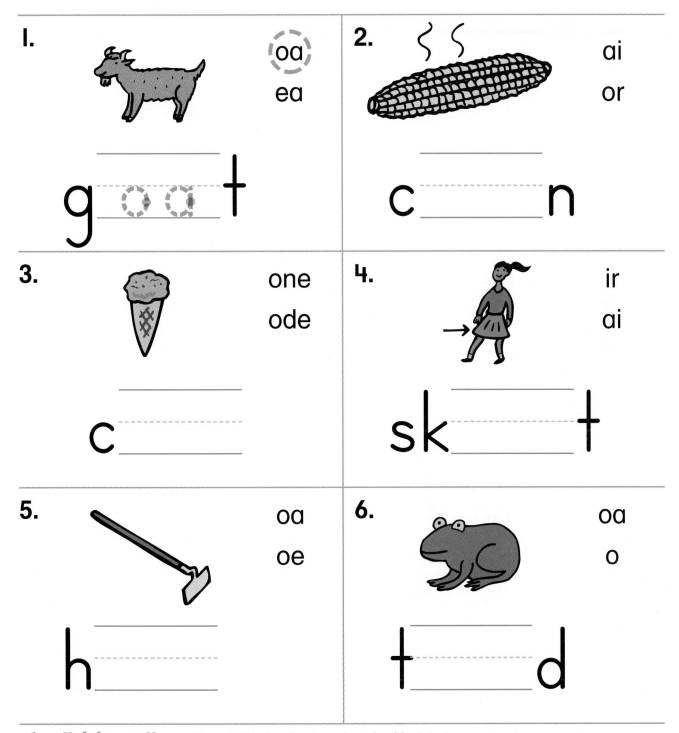

1. oa / ea

g o a t

2. ai / or

c ___ n

3. one / ode

c ___

4. ir / ai

sk ___ t

5. oa / oe

h ___

6. oa / o

t ___ d

Name_____

Fill in the circle in front of the word that names each picture. Write the word.

1. ● toe
   ○ told

   t o e

2. ○ bone
   ○ bore

3. ○ store
   ○ stir

4. ○ tried
   ○ tire

5. ○ hoe
   ○ home

6. ○ line
   ○ loaf

7. ○ first
   ○ flip

8. ○ boast
   ○ braid

9. ○ doe
   ○ dome

 Helping at Home Say words, such as: *mail, time, tie, mind, bird, go, home, core, for, loaf* and *toe.* Have your child say a rhyming word for each one. Then help him or her use the rhyming words to write a poem.

Name_____

Circle the missing letters. Then write them.
Read the word.

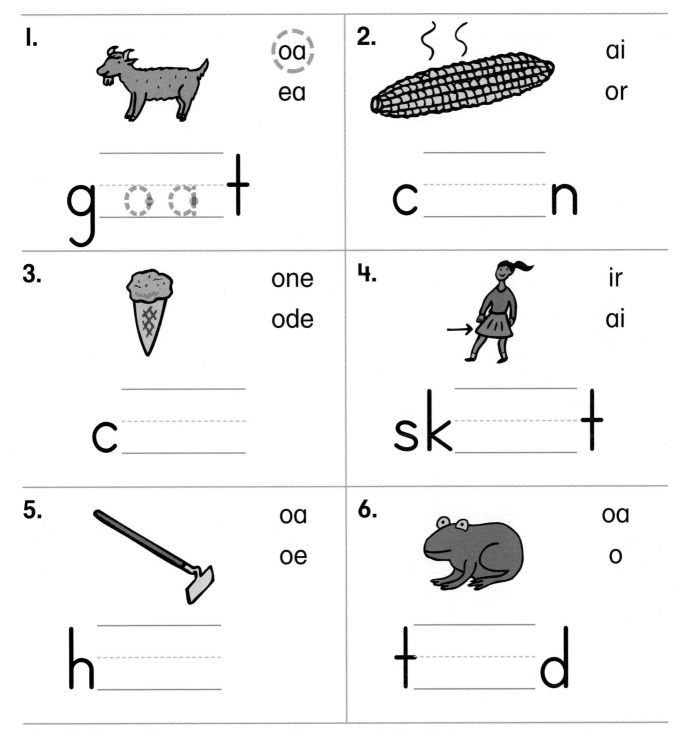

1. oa
ea

g o a t

2. ai
or

c _____ n

3. one
ode

c _____

4. ir
ai

sk _____ t

5. oa
oe

h _____

6. oa
o

t _____ d

 Helping at Home Your child is learning to read words with *ai, ie, ir, o* consonant *e, or, ore, oa,* and *oe*. To reinforce the learning, together hunt through books your child is reading for any words that contain these letter combinations.

Name_____

Fill in the circle in front of the word that
names each picture. Write the word.

I. ● toe
○ told

toe

2. ○ bone
○ bore

_____

3. ○ store
○ stir

_____

4. ○ tried
○ tire

_____

5. ○ hoe
○ home

_____

6. ○ line
○ loaf

_____

7. ○ first
○ flip

_____

8. ○ boast
○ braid

_____

9. ○ doe
○ dome

_____

 Helping at Home Say words, such as: *mail, time, tie, mind, bird, go, home, core, for, loaf* and *toe.* Have your child say a rhyming word for each one. Then help him or her use the rhyming words to write a poem.

Jj

jet	job	jog	jam	jar
jump	jumps	just	jacks	jacket
jaw	jigsaw	juggle	jeep	joke
Joe	Joan	Jean	James	jail

J j

Circle the pictures whose names have the same beginning sound as **jaw**. Write **Jj**.

jaw

1. 	2.	3. 
4. 	5.	6. 
7. 	8. 	9. 

 Helping at Home To give your child practice with *j*, encourage her or him to play "Joan and Jim." Explain that Joan and Jim only like to do things that begin with *j*. Together, brainstorm some activities. Examples: ride in a jet, jog, jump rope, jump up and down, tell jokes.

Vv

van	vest	vote	visit	save
wave	cave	gave	five	dive
diver	drive	driver	alive	arrive
over	silver	leaves	cover	scarves

Name_____

Vv

Write **Vv** under each picture whose name has the same beginning sound as **vest**. Draw lines to match the letters.

vest

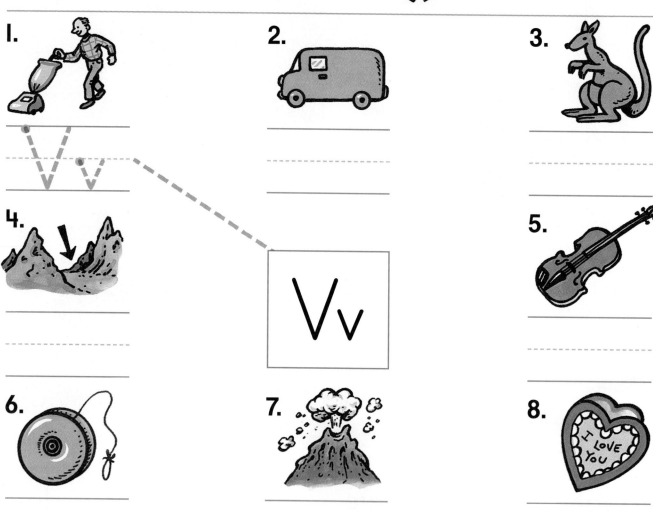

1.
_____

2.
_____

3.
_____

4.
_____

Vv

5.
_____

6.
_____

7.
_____

8.
_____

McGraw-Hill School Division

 Helping at Home To help your child practice *v*, encourage her or him to say sentences containing *v* words. For example, "Vincent drove the van to the village." Possible words for sentences: *visit, vase, valentine, very.*

A Dive in the Sea

by Judy Nayer
illustrated by Diana Magnuson

The divers have to go up now.
Jean swims to the boat. She
waves the bag of silver and grins.
The dive is over!

 Helping at Home Your child has read this book in school. Have him or her read it aloud to you. Then, together, look for pictures of sea creatures in books and magazines.

8

It is dawn. Jean gets in her van and drives over to the dock.

She is the first diver to arrive.

Jean sees the boat. She parks the van.

Then Jean sees a dark spot in the sand. Is it just junk? No, it's a trunk!

Jean tugs at the lock.

Silver! She waves for the divers to swim over and see.

Jean puts her bag on the boat and waits. At last all the divers arrive. The boat leaves the dock.

The boat stops. Jean gets dressed for a dive. She puts on a vest and a mask. She puts fins on her feet and a tank on her back.

A big eel swims at them!

Jean waves to the divers.

The divers hide in the cave. But the big eel just swims past.

Jean gets a float ball and ties it to her diver's rope. The ball floats on the waves.

"Jump in!" she tells the divers.

All of the divers fall over the side of the boat.

Jean floats down into the sea. At last her fins hit the sand.

The sea is full of life. A sea star waves all five arms.

J j

Name _____

Choose the word that completes the sentence. Write the word.

jam	jug	jeans	juggle	jig

1.

See Jim  .

2.

The pig did a _____ .

3.

He likes _____ on toast.

4.

Her _____ are torn.

5.

The _____ is full.

Helping at Home Give your child practice with words beginning with *j* by playing a riddle game. Example: Say, "I'm thinking of something that makes people laugh. Its name begins with *j*. What is it?" (joke)

Name_____

Color each picture whose name has the **v** sound as in **cave**.

I.	**2.**
3.	**4.**
5.	**6.**
7.	**8.**
9.	**10.**
11.	**12.**

 Helping at Home For practice recognizing words with *v*, help your child make a "*v*" valentine for another member of the family. Help him or her cut out pictures of objects whose names contain the letter *v* from old magazines. Then glue them onto a heart.

Name _____

Write the letters that stand for the beginning and ending sounds in each picture name.

1. _____ _____
   v   n

2. _____ _____

3. _____ _____

4. _____ _____

5. _____ _____

6. _____ _____

Name _____

Circle the missing letters. Then write them. Read the word.

1.

(v)
r

ca __v__ e

2.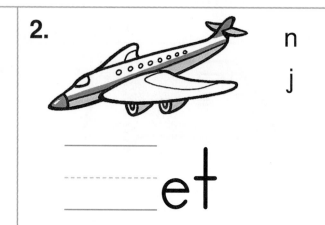

n
j

____ et

3.

ee
oa

b ____ t

4.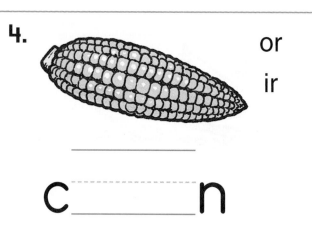

or
ir

c ____ n

5.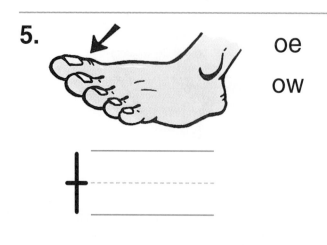

oe
ow

t ____

6.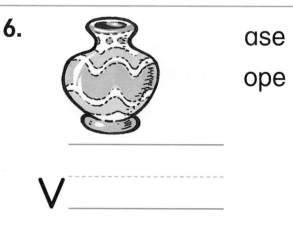

ase
ope

v ____

Helping at Home Your child has been learning to read and write words with *v* and *j*. With your child, take turns reading street signs, posters, books, advertisements, and comic strips. Encourage her or him to point out words that contain *v* and *j*.

sh

she	shell	shelf	sheep	sheet
shade	shake	shape	shark	share
ship	shop	shirt	short	shore
shine	shut	fish	dish	wish
wash	dash	trash	flash	splash
rush	brush	fresh	finish	slosh

sh

Circle the pictures whose names have the same beginning sound as **ship**. Write **sh**.

ship

1.	**2.**	**3.**
sh		
4. 	**5.** 	**6.** 
7.	**8.**	**9.** 

Helping at Home Give your child practice recognizing the *sh* sound by going on a hunt for items whose names begin with *sh*. Some things you might find include: *shirt, sheet, shed, shorts, shell, shelf*. If possible, have your child tape *sh* labels to the items.

sh

Write **sh** under each picture whose name has the same ending sound as **flash**. Draw lines to match the letters.

flash

I.

s h

2.

3.

4.

sh

5.

6.

7.

8.

 Helping at Home Your child is learning to read words that end with *sh*. Help your child practice *sh* words by playing an action game. Say some action words, some of which end in *sh*. If the word ends in *sh*, your child should pantomime the action. Examples: *brush, hop, jump, rush, fall,* and *hush.*

sh

Name_____

Name each picture. If the name begins with the sound of **sh**, write **sh** on the first line. If it ends with the sound of **sh**, write **sh** on the second line.

1.

sh
_____ _____

2.

_____ _____

3.

_____ _____

4.

_____ _____

5.

_____ _____

6.

_____ _____

McGraw-Hill School Division

 Helping at Home To give your child practice with *sh* words, teach her or him the tongue-twister "She sells seashells by the seashore." Then encourage your child to name other items whose names contain *sh* and to include them in the tongue-twister.

ch
tch

chin	chip	check	cheese	chase
chair	chimp	chore	chunk	chess
such	much	each	peach	rich
reach	beach	branch	bench	porch
lunch	bunch	crunch	spinach	sandwich
catch	match	latch	patch	scratch
watch	itch	ditch	pitch	switch

ch

Name _____

Circle the pictures whose names have the same beginning sound as **cheese**. Write **ch**.

cheese

1.	2.	3.
4.	5.	6.
7.	8.	9.

 Helping at Home Your child is learning to recognize words that begin with the letters *ch*. To practice this skill, say some words and have your child chirp like a bird if the word begins like *chirp*. Possible words include: *chase, child, chime, chop, cheek, chin.*

122   Introducing /ch/*ch*

McGraw-Hill School Division

ch

Name _____

Write **ch**. Color each picture whose name has the same ending sound as **bunch**.

bunch

 Helping at Home Your child is learning words that end with the letters *ch*. Help your child discover other words that end like *beach*. Together look through magazine and newspaper ads for items whose names end in *ch*. Possible items: *wrench, can of spray starch, peach, bunch of bananas.*

tch

Name _____

Write **tch** under each picture whose name has the same ending sound as **catch**. Draw lines to match the letters.

catch

1.

tch

2.

3.

4.

tch

5.

6.

7.

8.

McGraw-Hill School Division

Helping at Home To help your child practice *tch*, say these words and ask your child to respond with rhyming words in the same word family: *itch (pitch, ditch, hitch, switch), catch (scratch, batch, match, latch, hatch),* and *hutch (crutch, Dutch).*

Introducing /ch/ *tch*

If a Chimp Is on Your Porch

by Louisa Ernesto
illustrated by Shelley Dieterichs

If a chimp is on your porch, and if she likes her lunch . . . **watch it!**

She will ask a bunch of chimps to dinner.

Helping at Home Your child has read this book in school. Help him or her to read it aloud to you. Then talk about all the funny things the book says to do if you find a chimp on your porch.

8

If a chimp is on your porch, she
will want to sit.

Let her sit on your chair.

You can sit on the bench.

2

You can eat your spinach.

7

If a chimp is on your porch, she
will want to eat.

Let her have your lunch . . .
   your fish sandwich,
   your chunk of cheese,
   your dish of chips,
   your fresh peach,
   and much, much more!

If a chimp is on your porch, she
will want to run.

   Chase her!

   Now switch.

   Let her chase you.
   But do not let her catch you!

6

3

If a chimp is on your porch, she
will want to watch TV.

Let her switch it on.
Let her switch it off.
Let her share your popcorn, too.
Crunch, crunch, crunch!

4

If a chimp is on your porch, she
will want to do your chores.

Let her wash.
She will splash a little.
She will splash a lot.
You can clean up.

5

sh

Name _____

Name each picture. Draw a line to the **shell** if the name begins with **sh**. Draw a line to the **flash** if the name ends with **sh**.

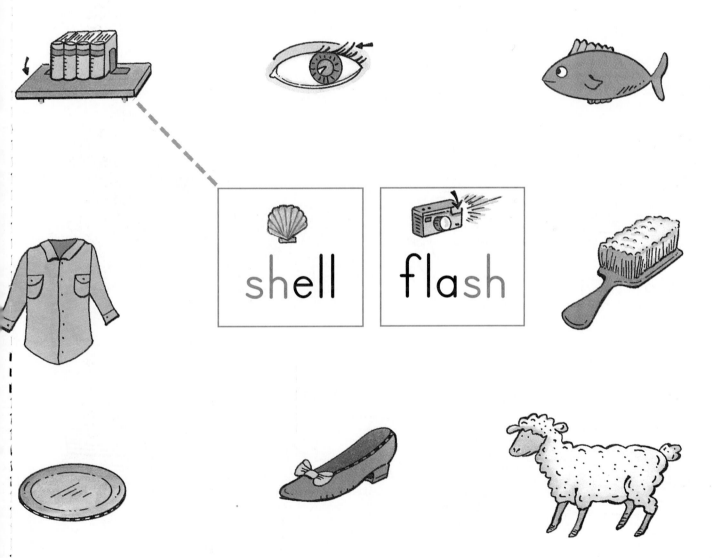

shell   flash

 Helping at Home Have your child print *sh* on a small card. Then write the following letter groups, each on a different card: *are, ip, op, ort, irt, fre, lea, ru, di*. Have your child put the cards together to form these words: *share, ship, shop, short, shirt, fresh, leash, rush, dish*.

ch

Name _____

Color the pictures whose names start with **ch** [red].
Color the pictures whose names end with **ch** [blue].

1.

2.

3.

4.

5.

6.

7.

8.

9.

10.

11.

12.

 Helping at Home Play a game with your child making silly sentences using words with *ch*. For example, *The chimp chews a bunch of cherries.*

McGraw-Hill School Division

tch

Name_____

Choose the word that completes the sentence. Write the word.

| catch | ditch | patch | Watch | match |

1.

The shirt has a _patch_ .

2.

I made a _____ .

3.

_____ me run.

4.

The dog can _____ .

5.

He is in a _____ .

 Helping at Home Play "Mix and Match." Write each of these words on two cards: *catch, watch, match, pitch, patch,* and *ditch.* Place the cards face down. Have your child turn over two cards and read the words. If the words match, your child keeps the cards.

Name _____

Circle the word that names each picture.
Write the word.

1. porch ⬯	**2.** sand / shell	**3.** fish / glass
porch		
4. hive / five	**5.** jacket / jeep	**6.** soap / sap
7. bore / fork	**8.** hat / hatch	**9.** girl / gift

McGraw-Hill School Division

🏠 **Helping at Home** Have your child print *ch* and *tch* on two small cards. Then write the following words, each on a different card: *in, ben, ma, air, bun, pa, bran*. Have your child put the cards together to form and read aloud words such as: *inch, chin, bench, match, chair, bunch, patch, branch.*

tch

Name _____

Choose the word that completes
the sentence. Write the word.

catch   ditch   patch   Watch   match

1.

The shirt has a ___p a t c h___ .

2.

I made a _____ .

3.

_____ me run.

4.

The dog can _____ .

5.

He is in a _____ .

 Helping at Home Play "Mix and Match." Write each of these words on two cards: *catch,*
watch, match, pitch, patch, and *ditch.* Place the cards face down. Have your child turn over two
cards and read the words. If the words match, your child keeps the cards.

Circle the word that names each picture.
Write the word.

1.  (porch) deer

porch

2.   sand shell

_____

3.   fish glass

_____

4.   hive five

_____

5.   jacket jeep

_____

6.   soap sap

_____

7.   bore fork

_____

8.   hat hatch

_____

9.   girl gift

_____

 Helping at Home Have your child print *ch* and *tch* on two small cards. Then write the following words, each on a different card: *in, ben, ma, air, bun, pa, bran*. Have your child put the cards together to form and read aloud words such as: *inch, chin, bench, match, chair, bunch, patch, branch*.

th

the	then	them	these	those
that	than	thank	this	thin
think	thick	third	three	thunder
with	bath	moth	teeth	north
month	fifth	other	father	brother
mother	rather	another	together	farther

th

Name _____

Write **th** under each picture whose name has the same beginning sound as **thin**. Draw lines to match the letters.

thin

1.

th

2.

3.

4.

th

5.

6.

7.

8.

Helping at Home Tell your child you are going to say some words with the *th* sound. If a word begins with the same sound as *thumb*, have your child make the thumbs-up sign. Possible words include: *theater, theme, thank, thunder, thick, thistle, throat.*

134   Introducing /th/ *th*

Name _____

th

Circle the pictures whose names have the sound of **th** as in **brothers**. Write **th**.

brothers

1. _____
   _____

2. _____
   _____

3. _____
   _____

4. _____
   _____

5. _____
   _____

6. _____
   _____

7. _____
   _____

8. _____
   _____

9. _____
   _____

Name _____

Write **th** under each picture whose name has the same ending sound as **teeth**. Draw lines to match the letters.

teeth

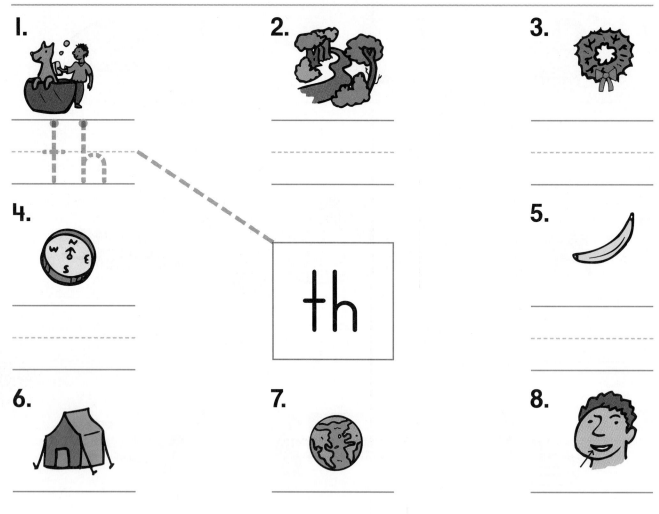

1.

2.

3.

th

4.

5.

6.

7.

8.

McGraw-Hill School Division

 Helping at Home Your child is learning to recognize words that end with *th*. For practice, ask your child riddles whose answers end with *th*. Examples: It hangs on a door. *(wreath)* It looks like a butterfly. *(moth)* You brush these twice a day. *(teeth)*.

wh

what	when	where	which
white	while	whale	wheel
whirl	wharf	whack	whisper
whisker	wheat	whether	whenever

wh

Name _____

Write **wh**. Color each picture whose name begins like **whisper**.

whisper

 Helping at Home With your child, write *wh* on a card. Write the following on individual cards: *at, en, ere, isker, ale, isper, isk, ip, eat,* and *eel.* Have him or her combine the *wh* card with each of the other cards to make words that begin with *wh*. Say the words.

When Walter Went to Sea

by Robin Bloksberg
pictures by Cheryl Hanna

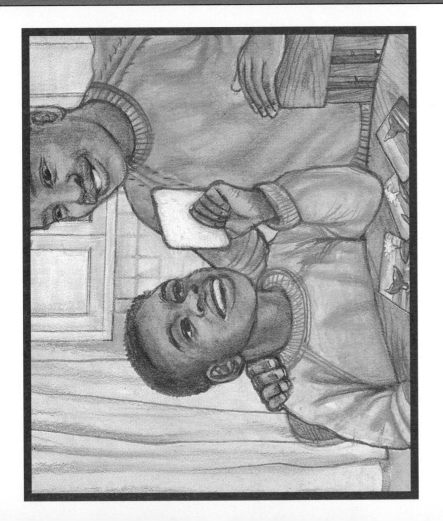

Walter was glad that he saw a whale. He wished his father had, too.

Then, a week after the trip, his dad did see Walter's whale after all!

 Helping at Home Your child has read this book. Have him or her read it aloud. Then, together, you might want to look for pictures of sea creatures in books and magazines.

8

Walter went to fish with his father.
They went to the wharf.

"Which boat do we get on?"
Walter asked his dad.

"That big white one," his
father said.

McGraw-Hill School Division

Walter ran to get his father. "I saw
a whale!" he said.

"What?" his dad asked. His dad
ran with him to see the whale. But
it was not there.

"Jump, whale," Walter whispered.
But the whale didn't jump another
time.

A man with thick whiskers helped Walter and his dad onto the boat. Other people got on, too. Then the boat left the wharf.

"When will I get to fish?" asked Walter.

"Soon!" his father said.

Then . . . .

Whack!
"What was that?"

It was a big tail! Walter saw a whale leap out of the water.

"Wow!" he said. "It is better to see this than to catch a fish!"

The boat went farther and farther. Then it stopped. People put their lines in the water.

Dad got a fish. A girl in a white jacket got three fish. Walter felt a tug on his line.

"I think it's a big one!" he said. But it wasn't a fish at all.

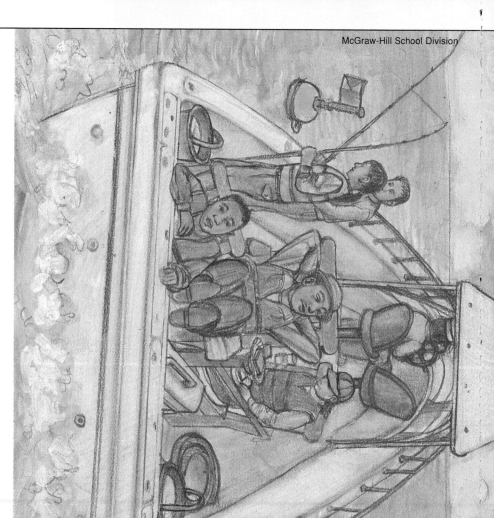

Then the boat started for home. Walter watched the man at the wheel for a while.

The other people had lunch. But Walter just stared at the water.

th

Name _____

Color the pictures whose names have the sound of **th** as in **bath**.

1.

2.

3.

4.

5.

6.

7.

8.

9.

10.

11.

12.

Helping at Home Play a category game to practice the sound of *th*. Name a category such as "things used for sewing" and have your child respond with words with *th* such as *cloth, thread,* and *thimble*. Another category is family members: *mother, father, brother, grandfather*.

Name_____

Choose the word that completes the sentence. Write the word.

| whiskers | Where | white | wheat | whale |

I.
The stripes are black and __white__.

2.
The _____ is big.

3.
_____ is Pat's dog?

4.
The cat has _____ .

5.
The _____ is tall.

 Helping at Home Print these tongue twisters on a sheet of paper and have your child read them aloud: *Which whale can whine? Which wheels whirled?* Have your child repeat each tongue twister several times. Then work together to make up other tongue twisters with *wh*.

McGraw-Hill School Division

Name_____

Fill in the circle in front of the missing letters.
Then write them. Read the word.

1.  ● wh ○ ch

 wheel

2. ○ tch ○ th

tee____

3.  ○ wh ○ th

____isper

4. ○ ch ○ th

fa____er

5.  ○ ose ○ ole

p____

6. 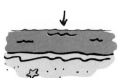 ○ ore ○ ave

w____

Helping at Home Your child has learned to read and write words that begin with *wh*. Some of these are question words–*who, what, when, where,* and *why.* Play a guessing game with your child asking questions with these words.

Name _____

Circle the word that names each picture.

1.

what   (whale)

2.

bath   bait

3.

care   chair

4.

shirt   chirp

5.
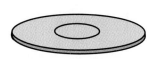

dish   ditch

6.

cane   cave

7.

jet   shed

8.

cold   coat

9.

watch   wash

McGraw-Hill School Division

Qu
qu

quit	quilt	quick	quack	quart
queen	quite	quiet	squirt	squint
square	squash	squat	squid	squirm

Qu
qu

Write **Qu** and **qu**. Color each picture whose name begins like **quail**.

quail

Qu   qu

Helping at Home Your child is learning to recognize words that begin with *qu*. Fold a sheet of paper into four sections. Then have your child make a "*qu* Quilt" by drawing a picture in each square whose name begins with the same sound as *quilt*. Possibilities: *quarter*, *queen*, and *quart of milk*.

McGraw-Hill School Division

Xx

ax	tax	wax	fox	box
fix	mix	six	next	text
exit	extra	exact	explore	explain
relax	boxes	waxed	mixer	sixteen

Name_____

Xx

Circle the pictures whose names have the same ending sound as **sax**. Write **Xx**.

sax

1. 	2.	3. 
4. 	5. 	6. 
7. 	8. 	9. 

Helping at Home To help your child practice the sound of *x* at the end of a word, have your child complete these sentences with a rhyming word. Be sure to emphasize the underlined word. Put that <u>fox</u> in the ___. *(box)* Just add flour to <u>fix</u> the ___. *(mix)* I got <u>wax</u> on my new___. *(sax)*

Name_____

Write **x** under each picture whose name has the sound of **x** as in **exit**.
Draw lines to match the letters.

exit  EXIT →

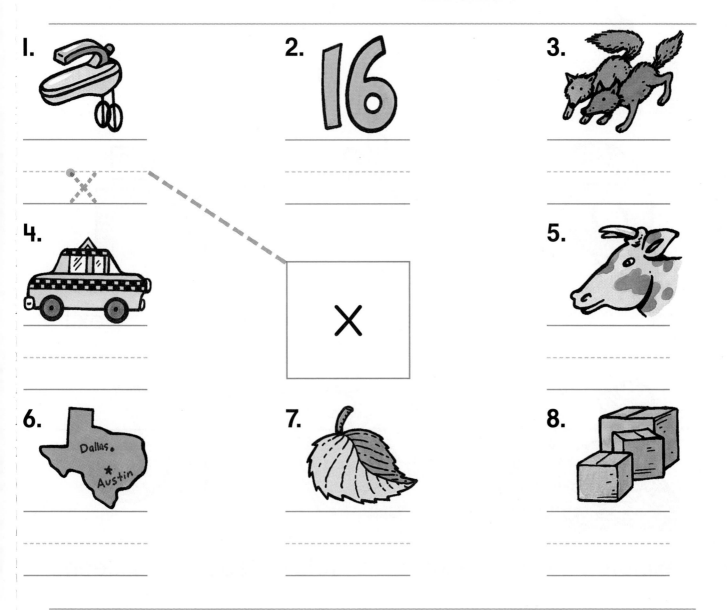

1.

2. 16

3.

4.

X

5.

6. Dallas.
★ Austin

7.

8.

 Helping at Home Your child is learning to recognize words with the letter *x* in the middle. Print the word EXIT in capital letters and draw a box around it to resemble an exit sign. Explain that exit signs are important in helping people find their way outside in emergencies.

Introducing /ks/*Xx*   151

Name_____

Circle the word that names each picture.

1.

(fox)   lock

2.

mixer   fixer

3.

locks   box

4.

six   sick

5.

wags   wax

6.

extra   exit

7.

explore   store

8.

exit   relax

9.

sacks   sixteen

 Helping at Home Say the following words: *next, ox, soft, oxen, quick, fix, wax, Texas, mix, quarter, tax, explore, boxes, six, relax, wave, sixteen,* and *ax.* After you say each word, tell your child to make an *x* with his or her fingers if the word contains the sound of *x.*

McGraw-Hill School Division

Fox, Tip-Top Truck Driver

by Janey Block
illustrated by Jeff LeVan

Fox is a tip-top truck driver.
He likes his job. But this time when
the sun comes up, Fox will not
explore. He will pick up no boxes
or pals. This time he will RELAX!

8

2

Fox drives a truck. He likes his job. When the sun comes up, Fox starts. He picks up boxes. He drives onto Wax Street at Queen Square. He gets off at Exit Six.

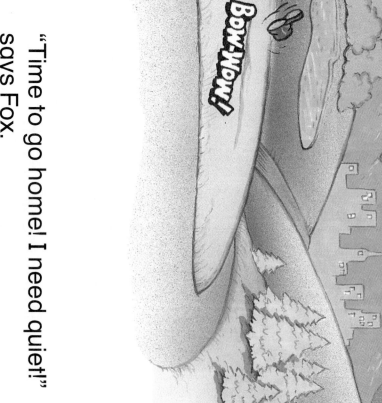

"Time to go home! I need quiet!" says Fox.

Fox drops off six dogs, three sheep, and six ducks. He drives past Exit Six and onto Wax Street at Queen Square. He drives home!

7

Fox grins. "I'm a tip-top truck driver. I like my job. But I want to see more. I want to explore."

Fox hears, "Quack! Quack!" He sees six ducks. They are his pals.

"We want to explore," the ducks explain.

"Hop in. Let's go," says Fox.

Fox and his pals drive past Exit Sixteen. Fox sees more. He hears more, too. He hears much too much!

Fox and the ducks drive past Exit Ten. Next Fox hears, "Baa! Baa!" He sees three sheep. They are his pals.

"We want to explore, too," the sheep explain.

"Hop in. Let's go," says Fox.

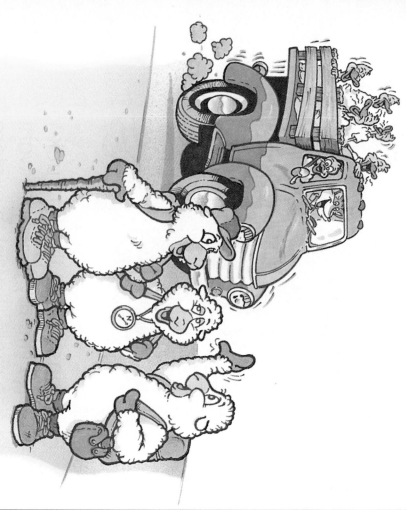

Fox, the six ducks and the three sheep drive and drive. Next Fox hears, "Bow-wow! Bow-wow!" He sees six dogs. They are his pals.

"We want to explore, too," the dogs explain.

"Hop in. Let's go," says Fox.

qu

Name_____

Color the pictures whose names have the sound of **qu** as in **squid**.

1.

2.

3.

4.

5.

6.

7.

8.

9.

10.

11.

12.

 Helping at Home Your child is learning words that have *qu*. Give your child practice by playing this word association game. Say *qu* words and ask your child to respond with words that begin with the same sound as *quiet*, such as: *king (queen), coin (quarter), blanket (quilt), bird (quail)*.

Name_____

Choose the word that completes the sentence. Write the word.

| fox | mailbox | wax | boxes | mixes |

1.

The _____ w a x _____ is red.

2.

What is in the _____ ?

3.

The _____ runs.

4.

Mom _____ the cake.

5.

What is in the _____ ?

 Helping at Home To help your child practice with *x*, give him or her a white crayon and a piece of white paper. Dictate these words for your child to write: *wax, box, ax, foxes, fix, mixer,* and *six*. To make the words magically appear, have your child paint over them with watercolors or food coloring.

McGraw-Hill School Division

Name _____

Write the letters that stand for the beginning and ending sounds in each picture name.

1. _____ _____

   qu   n

2. _____ _____

3. _____ _____

4. _____ _____

5. _____ _____

6. _____ _____

 Helping at Home Play a "Word Magic" game. Write the word *quill*. After your child reads the word, ask him or her to change one letter to make it something found on a bed. *(quilt)* Repeat this process, giving clues to help your child change *quick* to *quack, box* to *fox,* and *fix* to *six.*

Name_____

Circle the missing letters. Then write them. Read the word.

I.

n

(x)

_____

mi__er

2.

qu

wh

_____

_____een

3.

wh

th

_____

_____ale

4.

th

ck

_____

ba_____

5.

nk

ch

_____

bea_____

6.

sh

th

_____

_____orts

McGraw-Hill School Division

Yy

yes	yet	yell	yak	year
yarn	yard	yawn	yoke	yo-yo

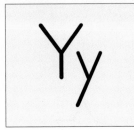

Name_____

Circle the pictures whose names have the same beginning sound as **yak**. Write **Yy**.

yak

I.	2. 	3. 
4. 	5. 	6. 
7. 	8. 	9. 

McGraw-Hill School Division

 Helping at Home Write the following word beginnings and endings each on a different card: *y/awn, v/est, sh/op, th/em, wh/ite, qu/een, y/ard*. Place the word beginnings in one pile and endings in another pile. Have your child choose one card from each pile and read each word he or she makes.

Zz

zip	zipper	zebra	zero	zone
fizz	quiz	fuzz	buzz	size
graze	amaze	amazed	freeze	breeze
sneeze	sneezed	squeeze	puzzle	Zigzag

Zz

Write **Zz** under each picture whose name has the same beginning sound as **zero**. Draw lines to match the letters.

zero O

1.

2.

3.

4.

Zz

5.

6.

7.

8.

 Helping at Home To help your child recognize the *z* sound, say the following words: *rip, cone, dipper, hero, boo,* and *room*. Ask your child to change the beginning sound in each word to *z* and to say the new word.

Zz

Name_____

Color each picture whose name begins with the sound of **z** as in **zip** or ends with the sound of **z** as in **fuzz**.

 Helping at Home Help your child read words ending with the sound of *z*. Write each of the following words on an index card: *fuzz, fizz, buzz, size, maze, prize*. Place the cards face down. Have your child turn over each card and read it.

Name_____

Zz

Circle the word that names each picture.

1.

pies   (prize)

2.

buzz   zero

3.

quiz   quilt

4.

puzzle   juggle

5.

maze   amaze

6.

mixer   zipper

7.

zebra   sneeze

8.

freeze   feet

9.

size   said

Helping at Home Play "Z Questions" with your child. Tell your child that you will ask some questions and that the answers will contain the letter z. For example: What do you get when you win a race? (*prize*). Where is ice cream kept? (*freezer*)

McGraw-Hill School Division

Zigzag's Sneeze

by
Cora Plexus

illustrated by
Doug Roy

Aaa, Aaa, Aaa . . . CHOO!

The bee tickles Zigzag's nose.

"Aaa, Aaa, Aaa . . . CHOO!"
Yes! Zigzag has sneezed!

 Helping at Home Your child has read this book at school. Have him or her read it to you. Then discuss the different ways that Zigzag's friends tried to help him sneeze.

8

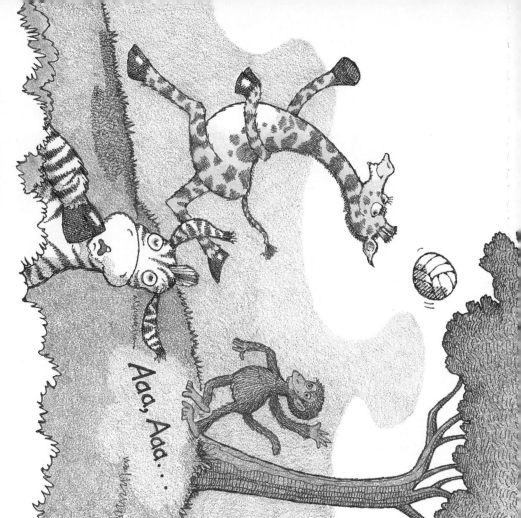

Zigzag the zebra needs to sneeze.

He starts, "Aaa, Aaa . . ."
But Zigzag just cannot sneeze.
What a puzzle!

Aaa, Aaa . . .

McGraw-Hill School Division

"We must help Zigzag," yells Yo-Yo.

"Do you hear that buzz?" asks Kit. BUZZ! A bee flies onto Zigzag's nose.

"I need to sneeze," sniffs Zigzag.

Kit grins. "We can make a zebra sneeze," he tells Zigzag.

Kit zips home.

"I need to sneeze!" Zigzag yells.
"A big sneeze or a little sneeze.
I do not care what size sneeze.
But I need to sneeze!"

4

Kit zips back. "Pepper will make you sneeze," explains Kit. "Just smell this."

Zigzag sniffs the pepper. "Aaa, Aaa . . ." he starts.

But no sneeze. Zigzag, the zebra, still can't sneeze.

McGraw-Hill School Division

"We must help Zigzag sneeze," says Yo-Yo. "Sniff this flower, Zigzag." Zigzag smells the flower.

"Aaa, Aaa . . ." he starts. But no sneeze yet! Zigzag the zebra still cannot sneeze.

5

Yy

Name _____

Choose the word that completes
the sentence. Write the word.

| yak | yarn | yo-yo | yolk | yellow |

1. Kittens like ___*yarn*___ .

2. The _____ has long hair.

3. She likes the egg _____ best.

4. His raincoat is _____ .

5. They share the _____ .

 Helping at Home Help your child practice identifying words that begin with *y*. Say two
words at a time. Ask your child to say *yes* if both words begin with *y*. Use these words: *yarn-yellow,
table-yam, yet-you, young-kitchen, quarter-yank, yell-yawn, yes-whale, yak-jump, yardstick-yolk*.

Zz

Name _____

Choose the word that completes the sentence. Write the word.

| fuzz | puzzle | Zip | freeze | zebra |

1.
Ponds  _freeze_ in the cold.

2.
_____ your jacket.

3.
The peach has _____ .

4.
Pat finished the _____ .

5.
We saw a _____ at the zoo.

McGraw-Hill School Division

Name_____

Fill in the circle in front of the word that names each picture. Write the word.

1. ○ awning
● yawn

y a w n

2. ○ free
○ three

3. ○ dime
○ dive

4. ○ wheel
○ will

5. ○ race
○ graze

6. ○ shorts
○ sorts

7. ○ quail
○ whale

8. ○ bench
○ bent

9. ○ yarn
○ barn

 Helping at Home Write silly sentences using some of the following words: *sneeze, yarn, explore, thunder, beach, splash, wave, jump, croak, cold.* Example: *He had to sneeze when he heard thunder.* Read the sentence aloud and invite your child to repeat it with you.

Name_____

Circle the missing letters. Then write them.
Read the word.

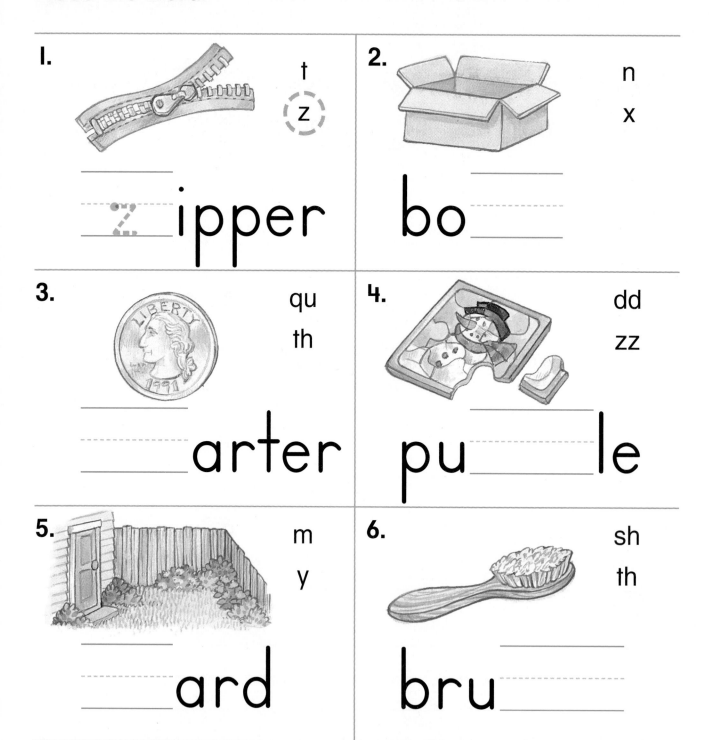

1.

t

(z)

___ipper

2.

n

x

bo___

3.

qu

th

___arter

4.

dd

zz

pu___le

5.

m

y

___ard

6.

sh

th

bru___

Helping at Home Write the following words on index cards or pieces of paper: *quarter, zipper, yellow, freezer, bath, sheet, shelf, jar,* and *soap.* Have your child read each word, find the object or color in the house, and then put the labels on the objects.

ng

ring	sing	wing	king	ding
fling	cling	bring	sting	thing
swing	string	spring	among	bang
rang	hang	sang	gang	fang
clang	song	long	along	strong
rung	lung	clung	stung	something

ng

Write **ng** under each picture whose name has the same ending sound as **ring**. Draw lines to match the letters.

ring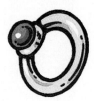

1.

2.

3.

ng

4.

5.

ng

6.

7.

8.

McGraw-Hill School Division

 Helping at Home Your child is learning to recognize words that end in *ng*. Write the following words on index cards or small pieces of paper: *bang, sang, king, wing, song, long, rung,* and *sung*. With your child, attach each card to a piece of string and then tie each string to a hanger to create a mobile.

The Land of Kings

by Eric Coates
illustrated by
Kevin O'Shea

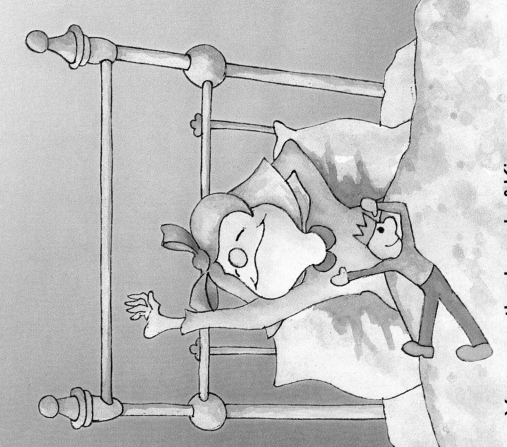

You saw the Land of Kings.
We hope that you had fun.
You had a long, long, long sleep,
and now your dream is done.

Helping at Home Your child has read this book in school. Help him or her to read it to you. Then ask your child to point out words in the story with the *ng* sound.

Hi! This is the Land of Kings.
We have all kinds of kings.

Some kings are small.
Some kings are tall.
Some kings are strong.
Some kings are long.

Some kings have sisters.
Some kings have brothers.
That king looks just like his mother!

Some kings stay home.
Some come along.
Some kings like to sing a song.

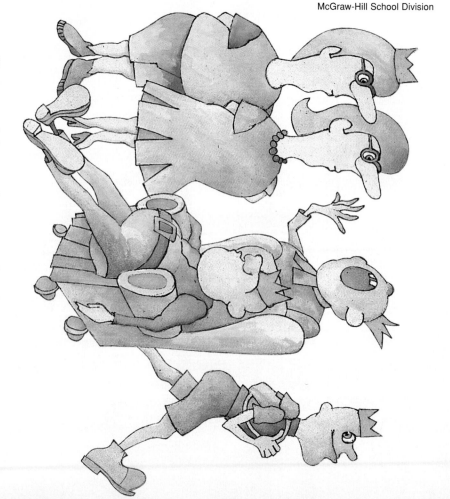

Some kings have rings.
Some kings have wings.

Some kings go clang,
And some just ding.

Some kings buzz.
Some kings fling.
Some kings ride on things
with wings.

Some kings can catch.
Some kings can pitch.
Some kings scratch
when some kings itch.

Some kings like swings.
Some kings like springs.
Some kings hang
from long, long strings.

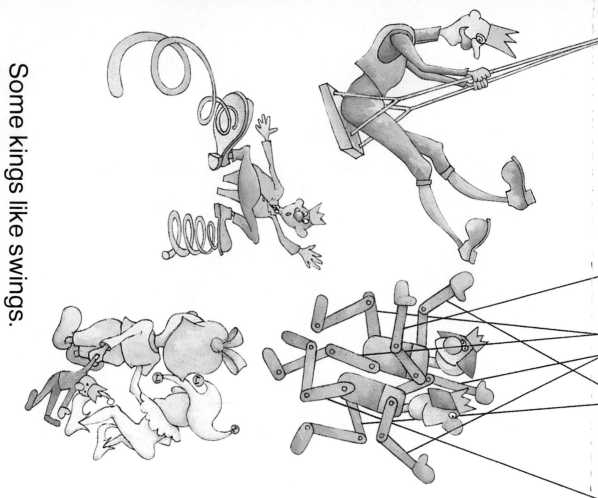

Some kings like scarves.
Some kings like hats.
Some kings like dogs.
And some kings like cats.

ng

Name _____

Color the pictures whose names have the same ending sound as **king**.
Write **ng**.

king

1. _____

n g

2. _____

3. _____

4. _____

5. _____

6. _____

7. _____

8. _____

Helping at Home To help your child practice the sound of *ng*, play "Bang the Gong." Use a pot lid and a spoon for a gong. Say words, such as: *along, buzz, strong, ax, think, song, among, brush, long, lunch, wrong, rung,* and *swung*. Have your child bang the gong if the word ends with *ng*.

Circle the missing letters. Then write them.
Read the word.

1.

tch

p

scra tch

2.

ng

ck

so_____

3.

er

s

zipp_____

4.

ng

x

fo_____

5.

ch

sh

spla_____

6.

l

th

tee_____

Helping at Home Your child has been learning to read and write words that end with *ng, er, x, th, tch,* and *sh*. Challenge your child to look through books and point out words with these endings.

ing

pushing	jumping	hunting	leaping
falling	soaring	peeking	howling
reaching	filling	curling	sleeping
digging	swimming	zipping	hopping
running	dropping	stopping	sitting
piling	making	carving	poking
nibbling	coming	chasing	taking
hiding	saving	storing	rising

ing

Name_____

Read the word. Add **ing**.
Write the new word to complete
the sentence.

float + **ing** → float**ing**

I.

peek   The girl is ⟨peeking⟩ .

2.

read   He is now _____ .

3.

fish   Mom and I are _____ .

4.

coach   Dad is _____ .

5.

pack   She is _____ .

6.

catch   Bob is _____ .

 Helping at Home Tape pages together to make a word book with your child. Write one of these words on each page: *jumping, singing, catching, fishing, eating, sailing,* and *reading*. Have your child paste magazine pictures to each page to illustrate the words. Read the book together.

McGraw-Hill School Division

ing

Name_____

Double the last letter.
Then add **ing** to make a new action word.

swim + **m** → swim**ming**

1.

hug + g + ing ⟶ *hugging*

2.

hop +___+ ing ⟶ _____

3.

pet +___+ ing ⟶ _____

4.

shut +___+ ing ⟶ _____

5.

run +___+ ing ⟶ _____

6.

sled +___+ ing ⟶ _____

 Helping at Home Your child is learning to recognize words in which the final letter is doubled before adding *ing*. Write each of the following words on a different card: *hugging, hitting, digging, tugging, sledding, hopping,* and *petting*. Ask your child to pick a card, read the word, and act it out.

ing

Name_____

Cross out the **e**.
Then add **ing** to make a new action word.

hid~~e~~ + **ing** → hid**ing**

1. smil~~e~~ + ing 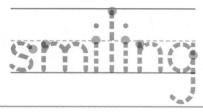	**2.** chase + ing	**3.** take + ing
4. bike + ing	**5.** share + ing	**6.** dive + ing
7. ride + ing	**8.** save + ing	**9.** shine + ing

McGraw-Hill School Division

🏠 **Helping at Home** Your child is learning to recognize words that end in *ing*. Write the following words on cards: *making, joking, poking, hiding, riding, diving,* and *waving*. Mix up the cards and then have your child read the words and identify the pairs of words that rhyme.

A Snug Little Nest

by Kana Riley
pictures by Cindy Brodie

Snow is piling up. It is reaching up over the wall. Where is Chipmunk now?

Chipmunk is snug. She is sleeping. Chipmunk is sleeping deep in her winter nest.

 Helping at Home Your child has read this book in school. Read it aloud together. Then have him or her tell you about the chipmunk's activities in his or her own words.

Chipmunk is digging. She is pushing the dirt and piling it up. What is she digging?

Chipmunk is making a deep little tunnel. Chipmunk is carving a snug little nest.

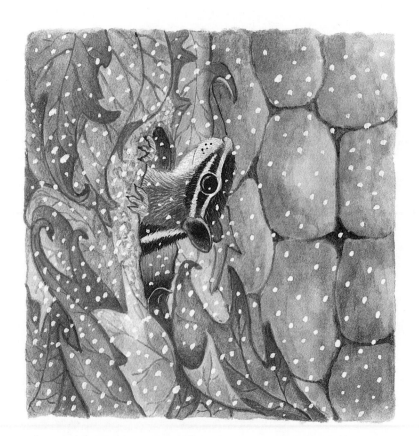

McGraw-Hill School Division

Chipmunk is peeking. She is poking her nose up to see. What does she find?

Flakes are falling. And winds are howling. White flakes are coming to cover her nest.

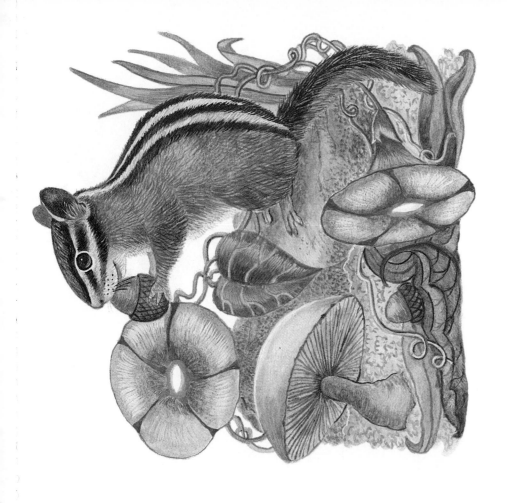

Chipmunk is poking. She is pushing the leaves. What is she hunting for?

Nuts! Chipmunk is nibbling a nut near her nest.

Chipmunk is filling her cheeks with seeds and nuts. Where is she taking them?

Chipmunk is hiding them. She is saving them. She is storing them deep in her nest.

4

Zip! Chipmunk is zipping over the wall. She is hopping across the grass. What is she running from?

A cat! A cat is leaping. A cat is hunting. A cat is chasing her back to her nest.

McGraw-Hill School Division

Darkness is falling. Chipmunk is running. What is she running from now?

An owl! An owl is soaring. An owl is hunting.

5

ing

Name _____

Read each word. Add **ing**.
Write each new **ing** word.

Just add **ing**

1. sailing

sail

2. _____

ring

Double last letter, add **ing**

3. _____

run

4. _____

tug

Drop **e**, add **ing**

5. _____

joke

6. _____

bake

 Helping at Home Play "Guess What I Am Thinking." Give your child a clue for an *ing* word. For example: This is what ducks are always doing (*quacking*). This is the opposite of throwing (*catching*). This is what we are doing at breakfast (*eating*). Ask your child to guess and write each word.

ing

Name _____

Choose the word that completes the sentence. Write the word.

| smiling | running | riding | sailing | sitting |

1. Jill is __riding__ her bike.

2. Ken is _____ for the ball.

3. Mike is _____ .

4. Karen is _____ on the bench.

5. Dad is _____ at me.

Helping at Home To help your child practice writing new words, say the following: *shopping, bring, size, hoping,* and *year.* Ask your child to answer by writing a word that rhymes with each word you say.

McGraw-Hill School Division

Name_____

Underline the word that completes the sentence.
Write the word.

I.

Stan is ___hiding___ under the plant.

hide

hides

hiding

2.

_____

Joan _____ in the band.

sing

sings

singing

3.

_____

The frog _____ across the pond.

hop

hops

hopping

4.

_____

Who is _____ up the hill?

run

runs

running

5.

_____

Bill was _____ on his bed.

jump

jumps

jumping

 Helping at Home To practice writing words that end in *ing*, write the following words: *win, run, bike, dig, hope, ring, stop,* and *wag.* Ask your child to rewrite each word with the *ing* ending. Remind him or her that some words need to drop a silent *e* or double the last letter before adding *ing.*

Name_____

Fill in the circle in front of the word that names each picture. Write the word.

1.
○ stitch
● switch

2.
○ swing
○ wing

_____

3.
○ moth
○ march

_____

4.
○ wheat
○ wheel

_____

5.
○ quit
○ quilt

_____

6.
○ breeze
○ zebra

_____

7.
○ frog
○ fox

_____

8.
○ hopping
○ hoping

_____

9.
○ biking
○ baking

_____

Helping at Home With your child, make a chart entitled "What I Like To Do." Put three columns with these headings on your chart: What; When; and Where. In the first column, have him or her write activities he or she enjoys and then fill out the other columns accordingly.

McGraw-Hill School Division

ed

needed	helped	reached	handed
fixed	finished	rested	cheered
coasted	hammered	crossed	yelled
stopped	planned	hopped	ripped
dropped	slipped	stirred	grinned
wiped	smiled	joked	waved
cared	saved	stared	hiked

ed

Name _____

Read the word. Add **ed**. Write the new word to complete each sentence.

cross + **ed** → cross**ed**

1.

help   I ~~helped~~ cut the apples.

2.

plant   Mom _____ flowers.

3.

land   The plane _____ on time.

4.

cheer   We _____ for the team.

5.

float   The boat _____ to shore.

6.

rest   I was tired, so I _____ .

Helping at Home Your child is being reintroduced to words that end with *ed*. Write these words on paper: *sawed, weeded, hammered, planted, cheered, floated,* and *reached.* Have your child pretend to do one of the actions listed above. Then guess which action he or she acted out.

ed

Name _____

Double the last letter. Then add **ed** to tell what happened in the past.

trip + p + **ed** → trip**ped**

1. dot + t + ed ⟶ dotted

2. wag + __ + ed ⟶ _____

3. stop + __ + ed ⟶ _____

4. plan + __ + ed ⟶ _____

5. hum + __ + ed ⟶ _____

6. skip + __ + ed ⟶ _____

 Helping at Home Make a word search. Using graph paper, fill in squares with the following words: *nodded, trapped, hugged, petted, pinned*. The words can go horizontally, vertically, or diagonally. After filling in the rest of the squares with random letters, help your child find the words.

ed

Name_____

Cross out the **e**. Then add **ed** to tell what happened in the past.

shar~~e~~ + **ed** → shar**ed**

1.

wav~~e~~ + ed

2.

joke + ed

_____

3.

smile + ed

_____

4.

choke + ed

_____

5.

care + ed

_____

6.

rake + ed

_____

7.

pile + ed

_____

8.

stare + ed

_____

9.

hike + ed

_____

Helping at Home To practice writing words with *ed*, have your child write a diary entry. Encourage him or her to tell what happened during the day.

McGraw-Hill School Division

THE LAST SPIKE

by Tom Fen

illustrated by Chi Chung

The train reached Jake and Will.
It coasted to a stop.

"You fixed the track," cheered the
riders on the train.

"Now it is time for us to ride, too!"
said Will.

"Just as we planned," smiled Jake.

 Helping at Home Your child has read this book in
school. Help him or her to read it aloud. Talk about what
it might have been like to build train tracks.

8

2

The train track needed fixing. Jake helped Will. Will helped Jake.

Will reached for a spike. He handed it to Jake. Jake put the spike on the track. Will hammered it down.

Jake and Will hammered spikes for a long time.

McGraw-Hill School Division

"The train!" yelled Will and Jake. "The train is down the track!" Jake stared. "I see it!" he yelled back.

They both waved.

2

7

Jake finished driving a spike. He stopped. He put down his hammer and wiped his neck. He needed a rest.

When they were finished, Will and Jake rested. They joked. They ate lunch.

Then they saw something on the track. Will cheered. Jake waved his hat.

"I'm glad we are almost finished,"
said Jake. "I am tired."

"Me, too!" said Will.
Will crossed his arms. "Three
more spikes. Then the track will
be fixed and the job will be over,"
he said.

Jake reached for his hammer.
"I want to ride the train when the
track is finished," he joked. Then
he hammered the next spike.

Will smiled. "Me, too," he said.
Then he and Jake hammered the
last spikes.

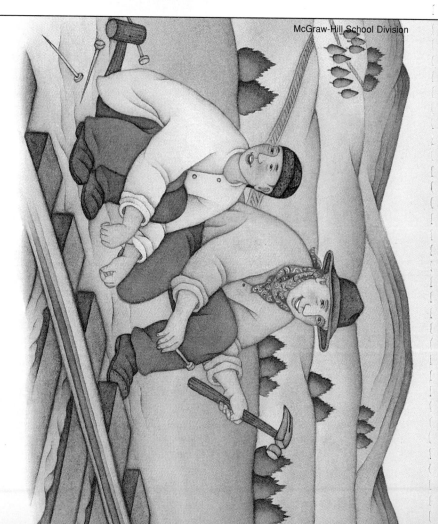

ed

Name _____

Read each word. Add **ed**.
Write each new **ed** word.

Just add **ed**

1.

reached

reach

2.

_____

rest

Double last letter, add **ed**

3.

_____

trip

4.

_____

skip

Drop **e**, add **ed**

5.

_____

shape

6.

_____

joke

 Helping at Home Your child has been taught different ways to add *ed* to verbs. Have your child write a note to a friend about what he or she did last week. Make sure he or she uses *ed* words.

Name _____

Underline the word that completes the sentence. Write the word.

1.

Bill wants to go _____fishing_____ .

fish
fished
fishing

2.

The frog _____ into the pond.

hop
hopped
hopping

3.

Can you _____ on the rope?

tug
tugged
tugging

4.

Dan _____ the seeds.

plant
planted
planting

5.

I went roller _____ .

skate
skated
skating

McGraw-Hill School Division

 Helping at Home Write the following words on separate cards: *skate, hop, bake, cheer, tug,* and *pass*. Put the words in a bag. Have your child reach in, pull out a card, and read the word aloud. Then have him or her add *ed* to the word and read it again. Continue until the bag is empty.

er

mother	brother	sister	whisker
singer	hanger	longer	shorter
gardener	catcher	helper	mixer
swimmer	winner	drummer	bigger
baker	diver	hiker	skater

er

Read each word in the box. Add **er**.
Write the new word to complete
a sentence.

small + **er** → small**er**

short	long	cold	thick	fast

1.

A kite string is ___longer___ than a jump rope.

2.

She ran _____ than Bill.

3.

Winter is _____ than summer.

4.

A branch is _____ than a twig.

5.

Ben is _____ than Sam.

Helping at Home To practice words that end in *er,* ask your child the following question, substituting a new word each time. What happens to *long* when you add *er*? It gets ___ (longer). After your child answers, have him or her write it down. Possible words: *quick, fast, tall, thick.*

McGraw-Hill School Division

er

Double the last letter.
Then add **er** to make a new word.

jog + g + **er** → jog**g**er

1.

swim + m + er ⟶

2.

shop +___+ er ⟶ _____

3.

win +___+ er ⟶ _____

4.

sit +___+ er ⟶ _____

5.

drum +___+ er ⟶ _____

6.

run +___+ er ⟶ _____

 Helping at Home Suggest that your child draw a picture of a *jogger*, a *winner*, a *drummer*, and a *swimmer*. Then have him or her label each picture.

er

Cross out the **e**.
Then add **er** to make a new word.

bik~~e~~ + **er** → bik**er**

1.

bak~~e~~ + er

2.

mine + er

3.

skate + er

4.

dive + er

5.

ride + er

6.

hike + er

7.

dine + er

8.

vote + er

9.

late + er

Helping at Home Help your child make an "All about Me" poster. The poster can have a self-portrait and the heading: I am a … Have your child write several *er* words to complete the sentence. Examples: *skater, reader, hiker*.

DIVER? HIKER? SWIMMER?

by Lea Martin

pictures by Bill Ogden

"Wow," said Jake, Beth, and Tom.

"Now we're all winners," said Jake. "Let's dig in!"

 Helping at Home Your child has read this book in school. Have him or her read it aloud. Then take turns acting out different sports or jobs for one another to guess.

Jake held one end of a big box.
His sister Beth held the other.
Their brother Tom opened it.

"What can we do with this stuff?"
he asked.

"I will get dressed up," said Jake.
"You tell me what I am."

Mom grinned. "I am a baker and
you are the baker's helpers. Get
the mixer. Get the pans. Let's bake
a cake!"

"What am I?" asked Jake.

"A diver!" said Beth.

"A swimmer!" said Tom.

"I'm a swimmer and a diver," said Jake. "You are both winners!"

"I am your mother!" said Mom. "And now what am I?" She held another hat. Then she put it on.

"You are a baker!" said Beth.

"Now what am I?" asked Jake.

"A gardener?" asked his sister.

"Not a gardener," said Jake.

"A hiker?" asked his brother.

"Yes!" said Jake. "I am a hiker."

McGraw-Hill School Division

Then Jake stopped. "What is that?" he said.

"It is a lot bigger than you!" said his sister.

"Are you a catcher?" asked Tom.

"A skater?" asked Beth.

"A drummer?" asked Jake.

er

Name_____

Read each word. Add **er**.
Write each new **er** word.

Just add **er**

1.

quicker

quick

2.

pitch

Double last letter, add **er**

3.

hot

4.

drum

Drop **e**, add **er**

5.

skate

6.

hike

 Helping at Home As you read with your child, have him or her point out words that end in *er*. Explain that some words ending in *er* have a base word such as **runner**. Other words ending in *er*, such as *father*, do not. Together, search for examples of both kinds of words.

Name _____

Fill in the circle in front of the word that completes the sentence. Write the word.

1.

We ___skated___ in the winter.

- ○ skater
- ● skated
- ○ skating

2.

The _____ sells rolls.

- ○ baker
- ○ baked
- ○ baking

3.

Who is _____ in the band?

- ○ drummer
- ○ drummed
- ○ drumming

4.

Tim _____ up the hill.

- ○ hiker
- ○ hiked
- ○ hiking

5.

Mom and I went _____ .

- ○ shopper
- ○ shopped
- ○ shopping

Helping at Home To help your child focus on words with *ing*, *ed*, and *er* endings, ask him or her to be a reporter. Have him or her interview family members about their day, and give a family news report at the dinner table. Then have her or him name the *ing*, *ed*, and *er* words.

McGraw-Hill School Division

Word List

a_e
ate
bake
cake
came
cane
cape
flakes
game
games
hate
made
make
mane
name
pale
same
skate
skates
take
takes
wake

are
bare
blare
care
Clare
dare
fare
flare
glare
hardware
hare
mare
rare
scare
spare
stare

e, ee
be
bee
deep
eel

feed
feel
feet
green
keep
me
meet
meets
need
needed
needs
see
seed
seeds
sees
sleep
street
tree
we're
weeds
week
weeks

ea
bean
beans
beat
clean
dream
east
eat
feast
hear
hears
heat
leaf
leap
least
meal
mean
meat
near
neat
pea
read

repeat
scream
sea
seal
seat
tea
treat

ai
aim
brain
drain
fail
hail
mail
nail
paid
pail
pails
pain
paint
plain

rain	I'm	time	go	or, ore
sail	inside	tire	gold	acorn
snail	kind	tried	hold	afford
tail	kinds		hole	before
trail	kite	**ir**	holes	bore
trails	lie	bird	home	born
train	life	birds	hope	cord
waist	like	dirt	hose	core
wait	likes	first	no	cork
waits	line	girl	nose	corn
	lines	Kirk	note	for
i, i_e, ie	miles	Sir	notes	forget
bite	mind	skirt	old	fork
blind	nine	stir	open	horn
cried	pie	swirl	poke	more
cries	pile	swirls	pole	or
find	pine	twirl	rode	popcorn
fine	ride		rope	score
fire	side	**o, o_e**	rose	scores
flies	smile	almost	roses	sore
grind	spike	alone	smoke	storm
hi	spikes	bold	so	tore
hide	tie	cold	stone	wore
hiker	tied	cone	told	
I'll	ties	fold		

216   Level B Word List

oa, oe

boast
boat
coat
float
floats
goat
goes
hoe
hoes
loaf
Moe
oak
oats
road
soak
soap
toad
toe
toes

Jj

jacket
jacks
jail

Jake
jam
James
jar
jaw
Jean
jeep
jet
jigsaw
Joan
job
Joe
jog
joke
juggle
jump
jumps
junk
just

Vv

alive
arrive
cave
cover

dive
diver
drive
driver
drives
five
gave
leaves
over
save
scarves
silver
TV
van
vest
visit
vote
wave
waves

sh

brush
dash
dish
finish

fish
flash
fresh
rush
shade
shake
shape
share
shark
she
sheep
sheet
shelf
shell
shine
ship
shirt
shop
shore
short
shut
slosh
splash
trash
wash

wish

ch, tch

beach
bench
branch
bunch
catch
chair
chase
check
cheeks
cheered
cheese
chess
chimp
chimps
chin
chip
chipmunk
chips
chore
chores
chunk
crunch

ditch
each
itch
latch
lunch
match
much
patch
peach
pitch
porch
reach
rich
sandwich
scratch
spinach
such
switch
watch

th
another
bath
Beth
brother

farther
father
fifth
month
mother
north
other
rather
teeth
than
thank
that
then
these
thick
thin
think
third
this
those
three
thunder
together

wh
whack
whale
wharf
what
wheat
wheel
wheeled
when
whenever
where
whether
which
while
whine
whip
whirl
whirled
whisker
whisper
white

Qu, qu
quack
quart

queen
quick
quiet
quilt
quit
quite
square
squash
squat
squid
squint
squirm
squirt

Xx
ax
box
boxes
exact
exit
explain
explains
explore
extra
fix

fox
mix
mixer
next
relax
six
sixteen
tax
wax
waxed

Yy
yak
yard
yarn
yawn
year
yell
yells
yes
yet
Yo-Yo
yoke
you're

Zz

amaze
amazed
breeze
buzz
fizz
freeze
fuzz
graze
puzzle
quiz
size
sneeze
squeeze
zebra
zero
Zigzag
Zigzag's
zip
zipper
zips
zone

ng

along
among
bang
bring
clang
cling
clung
ding
fang
fling
gang
hang
king
kings
long
lung
rang
ring
rings
rung
sang
sing
something
song

spring
springs
sting
string
strings
strong
stung
swing
swings
thing
things
wings

ing

carving
catching
chasing
coming
digging
driving
falling
finding
fishing
fixing
going

hiding
hopping
howling
hunting
jumping
leaping
making
nibbling
peeking
piling
poking
pushing
reaching
rising
roasting
running
saving
singing
sitting
sleeping
smiling
soaring
storing
swimming
zipping

ed

amazed
asked
boasted
cared
cheered
coasted
crossed
dressed
filled
finished
fixed
frowned
grinned
hammered
handed
helped
hiked
hopped
hugged
hunted
joked
landed
liked
lined

loaded
needed
opened
painted
picked
planned
planted
plopped
pulled
reached
rested
saved
smiled
sneezed
soaked
stared
started
stopped
tired
twirled
wanted
watched
waved
whispered
wiped

wished
yelled

er
after
another
baker
baker's
better
bigger
brother
brothers
campers
catcher
cover
dinner
diver
diver's
divers
driver
drummer
farmer
farther
father
flower

gardener
hammer
hanger
hangers
helper
helpers
her
hiker
longer
markers
mother
other
over
pepper
quicker
riders
runner
shorter
singer
sister
sisters
skater
summer
swimmer
under

Walter
Walter's
water
whisker
whiskers
winner
winners
winter

High-Frequency Words
comes
does
done
eyes
friends
one
paper
people
says
show
some
their
them

there
they
think
too
two
who
your

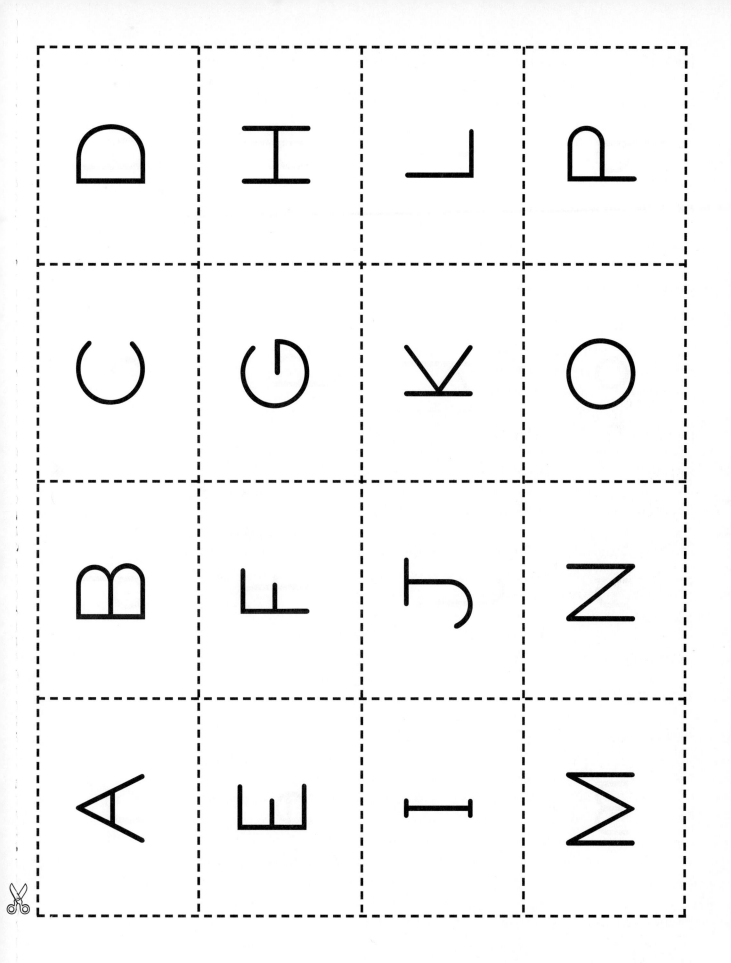

d	l	h	p
o	k	g	c
n	j	f	b
m	i	e	a

McGraw-Hill School Division

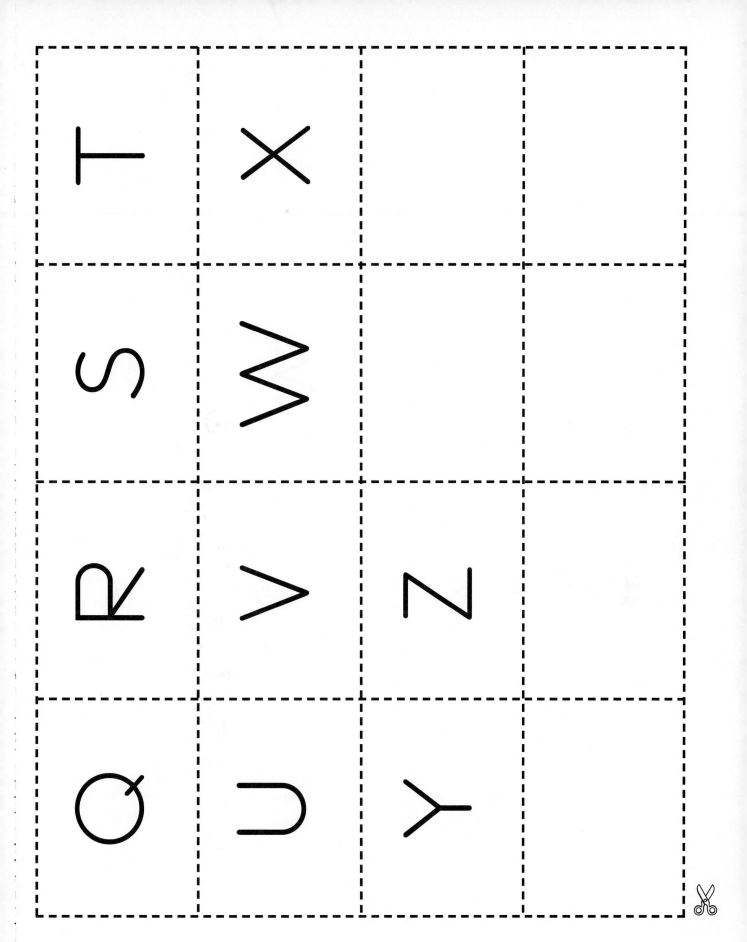

		x	t
		w	s
	z	v	r
	y	u	q